INTERNATIONAL SERIES OF MONOGRAPHS IN AERONAUTICS AND ASTRONAUTICS

DIVISION III. PROPULSION SYSTEMS INCLUDING FUELS

EDITOR: DR. B. P. MULLINS

VOLUME 4

SOME PROBLEMS IN THE THEORY AND ASSESSMENT OF TURBO-JET ENGINES

OTHER TITLES IN THE SERIES IN AERONAUTICS AND ASTRONAUTICS

DIVISION I. SOLID AND STRUCTURAL MECHANICS

Vol. 1. SAVIN — Stress Concentration around Holes
Vol. 2. GOL'DENVEIZER — Theory of Elastic Thin Shells
Vol. 3. NOWACKI — Thermoelasticity
Vol. 4. COX — The Buckling of Plates and Shells
Vol. 5. MORLEY — Skew Plates and Structures
Vol. 6. MANSFIELD — The Bending and Stretching of Plates

DIVISION II. AERODYNAMICS

Vol. 1. SCORER — Natural Aerodynamics
Vol. 2. LANDAHL — Unsteady Transonic Flow
Vol. 3. GUDERLEY — The Theory of Transonic Flow
Vol. 4. LOITSYANSKI — Mechanics of Liquids and Gases

DIVISION III. PROPULSION SYSTEMS INCLUDING FUELS

Vol. 1. PENNER — Chemistry Problems in Jet Propulsion
Vol. 2. GERSTEIN, LEFEBRE and DUCARME — Progress in Combustion Science & Technology Vol. 1
Vol. 3. RAGOZIN — Jet Propulsion Fuels

DIVISION IV. AVIONICS

Vol. 1. FLINDT — Aircraft Instruments and Automatic Control

DIVISION V. AVIATION AND SPACE MEDICINE

Vol. 1. WILLIAMS — Human Engineering and Aviation Medicine

DIVISION VI. FLIGHT TESTING

Vol. 1. BABISTER — Aircraft Stability and Control

DIVISION VII. ASTRONAUTICS

Vol. 1. ALPERIN, STERN and WOOSTER (Eds.) — Vistas in Astronautics 1.
Vol. 2. ALPERIN, GREGORY — Vistas in Astronautics 2
Vol. 3. DRAPER, WRIGLEY and HOVORKA — Intertial Guidance
Vol. 4. NIKOLAYEV — Thermodynamic Assessment of Rocket Engines

DIVISION VIII. MATERIALS, SCIENCE AND ENGINEERING

Vol. 1. HARRIS — Metallic Fatigue

DIVISION IX. SYMPOSIA

Vol. 1. KARMAN (Chairman of Editorial Committee) — Advances in Aeronautical Sciences (Vols. 1. & 2.)
Vol. 2. ALPERIN and SUTTON — Advanced Propulsion Systems
Vol. 3. DEVIENNE (Ed.) — Rarefied Gas Dynamics
Vol. 4. HOFF and VINCENTI — Aeronautics and Astronautics — Durand Centennial Conference
Vol. 5. PLANTEMA and SCHIJVE — Full Scale Fatigue Testing of Aircraft Structures
Vol. 6. BROGLIO — Current Research in Astronautical Sciences
Vol. 7. & 8. KARMAN — Advances in Aeronautical Sciences (Vols. 3. & 4.)
Vol. 9. PERRY — Flight Test Instrumentation
Vol. 10. BUCHANAN BARBOUR — Human Problems of Supersonic and Hypersonic Flight
Vol. 11. CASCI (Ed.) — Advances in Astronautical Propulsion
Vol. 12. BARROIS and RIPLEY — Fatigue of Aircraft. Structures
Vol. 13. DEARDS — Network Theory

INTERNATIONAL SERIES OF MONOGRAPHS IN AERONAUTICS AND ASTRONAUTICS

Some Problems in the Theory and Assessment of TURBO-JET ENGINES

by

K. V. KHOLSHCHEVNIKOV

Translated by

WILLIAM E. JONES

UNITED KINGDOM ATOMIC
ENERGY AUTHORITY

Translation edited by

B. P. MULLINS

DEPUTY CHIEF SCIENTIFIC OFFICER
MINISTRY OF AVIATION
FARNBOROUGH, HAMPSHIRE

A Pergamon Press Book

THE MACMILLAN COMPANY
NEW YORK
1964

THE MACMILLAN COMPANY
60 Fifth Avenue
New York 11, N.Y.

This book is distributed by
THE MACMILLAN COMPANY
pursuant to a special arrangement with
PERGAMON PRESS LIMITED
Oxford, England

Library of Congress Catalog Card Number 63–10043

This is a translation of the original Russian *Nekotorye voprosy teoriyi i rascheta turboreaktivnogo dvigatelya*, published in 1960 by Oborongiz, Moscow

MADE IN GREAT BRITAIN

Contents

Chapter II.

BASIS OF SELECTION OF ENGINE PARAMETERS FOR RATED FLIGHT CONDITIONS, TAKING INTO ACCOUNT AERODYNAMIC AND DESIGN DATA FOR THE COMPRESSOR AND TURBINE

Preface to the English Edition

This monograph develops from first principles the fundamental general theory of the design and performance of turbo-jet engines. Following a summary of the appropriate equations of conservation of energy and mass and using the gas laws and stoichiometric combustion relationships, equations for specific fuel consumption are derived.

Thermodynamic parameters expressing minimum specific fuel consumption, i. e. optimum engine conditions, are next discussed and the effects of operating conditions on these parameters are deduced.

The relationships between engine flight conditions and engine parameters defining compressor and turbine performance are derived in the second part of the monograph. Finally, the effects of changes in engine operating parameters on the dimensions of the engine components are evaluated theoretically.

Although the treatment of the subject-matter is necessarily mathematical it consists almost entirely of simple algebra and the monograph is quite suitable for first and second year technical college students of aeronautical engineering.

Farnborough, Hants.

B. P. MULLINS

Preface

In the present work the individual problems of the theory and assessment of turbo-jet engines are discussed, in particular the problem of optimum parameters. In order to determine the optimum values of the temperature of the gas and the rate of increase of pressure, equations are derived and conditions are specified for which both these parameters may be optimal simultaneously.

A substantial portion of the book is allotted to the coordination of the thermodynamic parameters of turbo-jet engines with aerodynamic and design data for the compressor and the turbine. It is recommended that this coordination be carried out with the aid of the complex parameter proposed by the author

$$\Pi = \frac{u_c \bar{G}_c}{\sigma p q (\lambda_t)}$$

In the process of the theoretical investigations by the author, an attempt has been made to analyse the individual problems in a generalized form, in order to impart a more general nature to the results obtained and thus to derive the possibility of utilizing them for adaption to turbo-jet engines in different circumstances, and also for extending them to gas-turbine engines of other types.

For implementing the operating data the author consulted Academician B. S. Stechkin, to whom he expresses his sincere gratitude.

The author expresses his thanks to Candidate of Technological Science O. N. Favorskii, Engineer L. A. Dmitriev, and Engineer N. I. Agapov, having participated in this work.

Mathematical notation

RELATING TO THE ENGINE AND ITS UNITS

R	Specific thrust in kg;
C_R	Specific fuel consumption, referred to engine thrust in kg fuel/kg thrust hr;
L_t	The work obtained from the turbine (without taking into account mechanical losses) in kg M/kg;
L_R	Total losses in a turbo-jet engine cycle in kg M/kg;
N_c	Power expended on the compressor in h.p.;
N_t	Power expended on the turbine, in h.p.;
η_e	Brake horse power efficiency of a turbo-jet engine;
η_{flight}	Flight efficiency of a turbo-jet engine;
η_o	Total efficiency of a turbo-jet engine;
η_c^*	Efficiency of compressor with respect to parameters of throttled flow;
η_t^*	Efficiency of turbine with respect to parameters of throttled flow;
η_m	Mechanical efficiency;
η_c	Coefficient of completeness of combustion;
δ	Pressure coefficient in the end section of any element of the engine, equal to the ratio of the effective total pressure to the total pressure on entry into this element;
φ_v	Velocity loss factor in the expansion section of the jet pipe;
α	Excess air factor (with the relevant suffices it is also the angle of flow in the compressor and in the turbine);
L_o	The theoretically necessary quantity of air, in kg for the combustion of 1 kg fuel;
H_u	Calorific value of the fuel in cal/kg;
$\nu = G_g/G_a$	Ratio of the gas flow rate through the jet pipe to the air flow rate through the intake section of the compressor;
$\nu_g = G_{g.t}/G_a$	Ratio of gas flow rate on discharge from the turbine to the air flow rate through the intake section of the compressor;
F	Cross-sectional area of the engine ducting in m^2;
A	Mechanical equivalent of heat in kg M/cal;
$q = G_f/G_a$	Quantity of fuel supplied to 1 kg of air in the main combustion chamber;

Q — Quantity of heat liberated in the combustion chamber, in cal/kg;
h_h — Adiabatic heat transfer in the jet pipe, in cal/kg;
h_{n1} — Adiabatic heat transfer in the jet pipe for adiabatic expansion in the turbine, in cal/kg;
u — Peripheral speed (compressor or turbine), in m/sec;
n — Engine speed, in rev/min;
$\overline{d}$ — Relative diameter of hub;
D — Diameter in m;
$Y^* = \sqrt{(\Sigma u^2)}c_{ad}^*$ — Parameter for a multi-stage turbine;
h — Height of turbine blade, in mm;
γ_b — Density of turbine blade material, in kg/cm³;
z — Number of stages;
σ_p — Tensile stress in turbine blades from centrifugal forces, in kg/cm²;
χ — Ratio of the turbine blade cross-sectional area at the tip to the area at the root;

GAS-DYNAMIC AND AUXILIARY QUANTITIES AND FUNCTIONS

$\lambda = c/a_{cr}$ — Velocity coefficient;
a_{cr} — Critical speed, in m/sec;
$\pi(\lambda) = p/p^*$ — Gas-dynamic function;
$\tau(\lambda) = \frac{T}{T^*}$;
$q(\lambda) = \frac{G}{G_{cr}}$;
$f(\lambda) = \frac{\rho c^2 + p}{p^*}$;
$\delta_{cool} = G_{a.c}/G_a$ — Coefficient taking into consideration the cooling air flow rate;
n_t — Index for polytropic process in the turbine;
n_c — Index for polytropic process in the compressor;
φ_1 — Coefficient, taking into consideration the quantity from the overall quantity of air tapped off for cooling, entering the turbine section between inlet and outlet valve.
φ_2 — Coefficient, taking into consideration the quantity of air, from the overall quantity of air tapped off for cooling, entering the jet pipe.
R_a — Gas constant for air;
R_g — Gas constant for the gases;
$B = \frac{q_0}{T_g^* - T_c^*}$ — Coefficient in the equation for specific fuel consumption;
Φ — Shape factor of blades, taking into consideration the law of variation of the cross-sectional area along its height;

X Parameter in the equation for determining the ratio D_c/D_t;

k_o Safety factor with respect to tensile stresses.

SUFFICES

i On entry into the compressor;
c Compressor and on discharge from the compressor;
t Turbine and on discharge from turbine;
g In the combustion chamber (prior to turbine) and for gases through the engine duct;
Φ In a reheat chamber;
H Surrounding medium (atmosphere);
n Jet pipe and in its discharge section (or in the throat);
cr Critical parameters;
* Parameters of throttled flow;
a Axial flow;
cool Cooling flow;
ad Adiabatic process;
p Tensile stress in turbine blades;
b Blades.

CHAPTER 1

General Problems of the Theory of Turbo-jet Engines

1. Initial Equations and Conditions

Equations for Thrust and Specific Thrust

The basic parameters characterizing turbo-jet engines are: (1) thrust and specific thrust; (2) hourly and specific fuel consumption.

Let us consider briefly the equations which will be used in future for determining these parameters.

The thrust of an engine, without taking into account external losses, can be determined, as is well-known, in the general case by the expression

$$R = \frac{G_g c}{g} - \frac{G_a V}{g} + (p_n - p_H) F_n, \tag{1.1}$$

where R is the thrust of the engine in kg;
G_g is the gas flow rate through the nozzle in kg/sec;
G_a is the air flow rate through the intake section of the compressor in kg/sec;
c is the velocity of discharge of the gas from the nozzle in m/sec;
V is the flight velocity in m/sec;
p_n is the pressure in a section of the nozzle in kg/m²;
p_H is the atmospheric pressure in kg/m²;
F_n is the area of the exit section of the nozzle in m²;

or

$$R = G_a \left[\frac{G_g}{G_a}\frac{c}{g} - \frac{V}{g} + (p_n - p_H)\frac{F_n}{G_a}\right]. \tag{1.2}$$

The thrust of the engine, for complete expansion of the gas to atmospheric pressure is

$$R = G_a\left(\frac{G_g}{G_a}\frac{c}{g} - \frac{V}{g}\right). \tag{1.3}$$

Here, the discharge velocity c is expressed by the equation

$$c = \varphi_v \sqrt{\left[2g\frac{k_g}{k_g - 1} R_t T_n^* \left(1 - 1/\pi_n^{(k_g - 1/k_g)}\right)\right]}, \tag{1.4}$$

where φ_v is the coefficient of loss of velocity (in the divergent part) in the nozzle;

π_n is the expansion ratio in the nozzle from the dynamic pressure in the nozzle throat to the external (atmospheric) pressure;

T_{thr}^* is the temperature of the throttled gas stream in the nozzle.

The magnitude of π_n depends on the expansion ratio in the compressor, the expansion ratio in the turbine, and the expansion ratio from the ram pressure, and it is determined by the expression

$$\pi_c = \frac{\delta_\Sigma \pi_c^* \pi_v}{\pi_t^*}, \tag{1.5}$$

where

$$\delta_\varepsilon = \delta_{\text{in}}\,\delta\;\delta_n;$$

δ_{in} is the dynamic pressure coefficient in the intake system;

δ_c is the dynamic pressure coefficient in the combustion chamber;

δ_n is the dynamic pressure coefficient in the nozzle from the turbine to the nozzle throat;

π_c^* is the expansion ratio in the compressor;

π_t^* is the expansion ratio in the turbine.

The expansion ratio of the ram pressure for an isentropic process is determined by the equation

$$\pi_v = \frac{1}{\Pi(\lambda_H)} - \left(1 - \frac{k-1}{k+1}\lambda_H^2\right)^{k/(k-1)}; \; \lambda_H = \frac{V}{a_{\text{cr}}}.$$

In the presence of a convergent nozzle, φ_v should not enter into equation (1.4), since in this case all the losses in the nozzle are evaluated by the coefficient δ_n.

In the presence of a divergent nozzle, φ_v should enter into equation (1.4) and in the implicit form (through π_n) also δ_n, whereupon φ_v evaluates the velocity losses in the divergent section of the nozzle.

The temperature T^*_{thr} of the throttled gas stream prior to the nozzle throat for an engine with a reheat chamber is equal to the temperature of the gas in the reheat chamber. In the absence of a reheat chamber it can be taken that $T^*_{thr} = T^*_t$, where T^*_t is the temperature of the gas after the turbine.

Consequently, in an engine without a reheat chamber, the temperature T^*_{thr} (in place of which we shall write T^*_t) is a function of the temperature of the gas prior to the turbine and the expansion ratio in the turbine π^*_t. If the index for a polytropic process of expansion in the turbine be introduced, then the connection between these values is expressed by the equation

$$T^*_t = \frac{T^*_g}{\pi_t^{*(n_t-1)/n_t}},$$

where T^*_g is the temperature of the gas prior to the turbine;

n_t is the polytropic expansion index.

The temperature of the gas T^*_t and the expansion ratio in the turbine π^*_t may be found by the equation expressing the work balance of the turbine and the compressor. First of all we shall consider the consumption balance for the working substance through the duct of a turbo-jet engine.

The quantity of air entering the combustion chamber is less than the supply of air passing through the intake section of the compressor in view of the transfer of part of the air for cooling the turbine, the bearings and the reheat chamber.

Thus,

$$G_{d.c} = G_a - G_{\text{cool}} = G_d \delta_{\text{cool}} \tag{1.6}$$

where $\delta_{\text{cool}} = \frac{G_{d.c}}{G_a}$.

Consequently

$$G_{\text{cool}} = G_d (1 - \delta_{\text{cool}}).$$

The leakage of gas directly from the compressor duct is also allowed for by the coefficient δ_{cool}.

The air for cooling can be withdrawn from an intermediate stage of the compressor, but in the work balance equation the air flow rate is written as the air flow rate reduced to the conditions of discharge from the compressor

$$G_{\text{cool red}} = \frac{G_{\text{cool}} L_{c1}}{L_c},$$

where $G_{\text{cool red}}$ is the supply of air withdrawn for cooling and reduced to the discharge conditions from the compressor;

L_{c1} is the work expended on the stages of the compressor, after which air is tapped off;

L_c is the work expended on the compressor.

A portion of the air going for cooling gets into the air-gas flow area (the section of the turbine between the inlet and outlet valves), as a consequence of which the quantity of gas on issuing from the turbine is

$$G_{g.t} = G_{a.c} + \xi_1 G_{\text{cool}} + G_{\text{f1}},$$

where ξ_1 is a coefficient, taking into consideration the quantity of air entering the air – gas flow area;

G_{f1} is the fuel flow rate.

The quantity of gas discharging from the nozzle is

$$G_g = G_{g.t} + \xi_2 G_{\text{cool}} + G_{\text{f2}},$$

where ξ_2 is a coefficient, taking into consideration the quantity of air reaching the nozzle from the cooling system, by passing the turbine;

G_{f2} is the fuel flow rate into the reheat chamber.

For an engine without reheat chamber we obtain

$$G_g = G_a[\delta_{\text{cool}} + (1 - \delta_{\text{cool}})(\xi_1 + \xi_2)] + G_{f1}.$$

If $\xi_1 + \xi_2 = 1{\cdot}0$, then $G_g = G_a + G_{f1}$.

When $(\xi_1 + \xi_2) < 1{\cdot}0$, then a leak of air occurs.

The fuel flow rate G_{f1} is connected with the air flow rate passing through the combustion chamber by the relationship

$$G_{f1} = \frac{G_a \delta_{\text{cool}}}{\alpha L_0}.$$

Consequently,

$$G_g = G_a \left[\delta_{\text{cool}} + (1 - \delta_{\text{cool}})(\xi_1 + \xi_2) + \frac{\delta_{\text{cool}}}{\alpha L_0}\right]. \tag{1.7}$$

Correspondingly, for a fuel flow rate into the reheat chamber

$$G_g = G_a[\delta_{cool}+(1-\delta_{cool})(\xi_1+\xi_2)]\left[1+\frac{1}{\alpha_0 L_0}\right], \qquad (1.8)$$

where α_0 is the overall excess air factor, taking into account the fuel supplies to the main and reheat chambers.

In order to determine the delivery of gas in the discharge section behind the turbine, we obtain

$$G_{g.t} = G_a\left[\delta_{cool}+\xi_1(1-\delta_{cool})+\frac{\delta_{cool}}{\alpha L_0}\right]. \qquad (1.8a)$$

The consumption balance quoted is of fundamental importance but reliable values for δ_{cool} and for the coefficients ξ_1 and ξ_2 are not known even today, and which, and moreover, strongly depend on individual special features of design.

The values enclosed in the square brackets in Formulae (1.7). (1.8) and (1.8a) can be respectively designated by ν, ν_1 and ν_t, Then

$G_g = G_a\nu$ for an engine without reheat chamber;

$G_g = G_a\nu_1$ for an engine with reheat chamber.

Similarly, the delivery of gas discharging from the turbine can be written in the form

$$G_{g.t} = G_a\nu_t.$$

The power of the gas turbine is expended on running the compressor, and also on driving the various units, on friction in the bearings of the turbine and of the compressor:

$$N_{t.g}+N_{t.a}=N_c+N_{t.u},$$

where $N_{t.g}$ is the power (internal) of the gas turbine obtained from the hot gases;

$N_{t.a}$ is the power of the gas turbine obtained from the cooling air passing through the turbine;

N_c is the power expended on the compressor;

$N_{t.u}$ is the power expended on driving units and on mechanical losses.

We shall relate the power obtained from the cooling air to the power $N_{t.u}$ and we shall denote

$$\eta_m = \left(1-\frac{N_{t.a}-N_{t.u}}{N_{t.g}}\right).$$

We express $N_{t.g}$ and N_c via the gas flow rate and by the internal work. For this, the gas flow rate through the turbine is expressed by means of equation (1.8a), but for $\xi_1=0$, since $N_{t.g}$ refers only to the hot gases:

$$\left(1+\frac{1}{\alpha L_0}\right)\delta_{cool}G_a L_t \eta_m = G_a L_c$$

or,

$$\left(1+\frac{1}{\alpha L_0}\right)\delta_{cool} L_t \eta_m = L_c \,. \tag{1.9}$$

Whence

$$T_t^* = T_g^* - \frac{L_c}{\left(1+\frac{1}{\alpha L_9}\right)\delta_{cool}\eta_m}\,\frac{66}{\frac{k_g}{k_g-1}R_g} \tag{1.10}$$

or,

$$\frac{T_t^*}{T_H^*} = \frac{T_g^*}{T_H^*} - \frac{\frac{k}{k-1}R}{\left(1+\frac{1}{\alpha L_0}\right)\delta_{cool}\frac{k_g}{k_g-1}R_g\eta_m}\,\frac{\pi_c^{(k-1)/k}-1}{\eta_c^*}\,. \tag{1.11}$$

We shall adopt the notations

$$a = \frac{\frac{k}{k-1}R}{\left(1+\frac{1}{\alpha L_0}\right)\delta_{cool}\frac{k_g}{k_g-1}R_g\eta_m}\,;\quad 2\,(\pi_c^*) = \frac{\pi_k^{(k-1)/k}-1}{\eta_c^*}\,.$$

The value of a depends on k_g and α and, consequently, on the temperature of the gas and of the air on entry into the combustion chamber, also on the expansion in the turbine. Moreover, into this value there enter the little-studied losses by cooling and on driving supplementary units. Finally, the index k for air should also, in principle, be taken as different, depending on the temperature of the air and on the expansion ratio. All the values enumerated should vary, depending on the flight conditions and on the operating regimes of the engine.

Usually, only change of α is taken into account in the calculations, and the remaining values are taken to be constant. The mean values of the coefficient a, used in the calculations, are equal to 0·875 – 0·885. The value $l\,(\pi_c^*)$ is proportional to the work expended on running the compressor, and should be determined by taking into account the variable specific heat of the air.

In the present work, the variation of specific heat in the process of compression and expansion is basically not taken into consideration, and only at the end of Chapter I is a comparison given of specific fuel consumptions and specific thrusts, obtained by taking into account and also without taking into account changes in the specific heat of air. After substitution of the symbols adopted we obtain

$$\frac{T_t^*}{T_H^*} = \frac{T_g^*}{T_H^*} - al\left(\pi_c^*\right). \tag{1.12}$$

The expansion ratio in the turbine is expressed by means of equation (1.12) in the following manner:

$$\pi_t^* = \frac{1}{\left[1 - a\dfrac{T_H^*}{T_g^*}\dfrac{2\left(\pi_k^*\right)}{\eta_t^*}\right]^{k_g/(k_g-1)}}. \tag{1.13}$$

In conjunction with this, equation (1.5) can be written in the form

$$\pi_n = \left(\delta_\Sigma \pi_c^* \pi_v\right)\left[1 - a\frac{T_H^*}{T_g^*}\frac{l\left(\pi_c^*\right)}{\eta_t^*}\right]^{k_g/(k_g-1)}. \tag{1.14}$$

For the convenience of theoretical studies, we shall denote equation (1.3) for the thrust of the engine by

$$R\left(\pi_n^*\right) = \sqrt{\left[\frac{2}{g}\frac{k_g}{k_g-1}R_g\left(1 - \frac{1}{\pi_n{}^{(k_g-1)/k_g}}\right)\right]}. \tag{1.15}$$

In addition, taking the index k for air as constant, we can replace the flight velocity by the expression

$$\frac{V}{g} = 1{\cdot}87 \cdot \lambda_H \sqrt{T_H^*},$$

where

$$\lambda_H = \frac{V}{a_{cr}}.$$

Equation (1.3) then takes the form

$$R = G_a\sqrt{T_H^*}\left[\nu\varphi_V\sqrt{\left(\frac{T_t^*}{T_H^*}\right)}R\left(\pi_n\right) - 1{\cdot}87\,\lambda_H\right], \tag{1.16}$$

where

$$\nu = \frac{G_g}{G_a}.$$

The specific thrust represents the thrust obtained from 1 kg of air admitted into the compressor, therefore

$$R = G_a R_{sp}.$$

Consequently,

$$R_{sp} = \sqrt{T_H^*}\left[\nu\varphi_V \sqrt{\left(\frac{T_t^*}{T_H^*}\right)} R(\pi_n) - 1{\cdot}87\,\lambda_H\right]. \qquad (1.17)$$

Expressions (1.16) and (1.17) are just as applicable to a complete expansion as to the use of a convergent nozzle for $\pi_n \geq \pi_{n\,\mathrm{crit}}$, if the appropriate value of $R(\pi_n)$ is taken for each case.

As a demonstration of this we shall make use of the expression for the propulsive force proposed by V. I. Babarin,

$$R = F_n P_H\,[f(\lambda_n)\pi_n - 1] - \frac{G_a V}{g}. \qquad (1.18)$$

where

$$f(\lambda_n) = (1+\chi_n^2)\left(1 - \frac{k-1}{k+1}\lambda_n^2\right)^{1/(k-1)}$$

As is well known, equation (1.18) is obtained from the condition that the discharge impulse is linked with λ_n, P_n and F_n by the relationship

$$\frac{G_g}{g}C + P_n F_n = f(\lambda_n) P_n^* F_n$$

The specific thrust can be determined by the formula

$$R_{sp} + \frac{F_n P_H}{G_a}\,[f(\lambda_n)\pi_n - 1] - \frac{V}{g},$$

by means of equation (1.18).

The air flow rate is determined from the relationship obtained above, $G_a = G_g/\nu$.

On the other hand, the gas flow rate can be written in the form

$$G_g = \frac{F_n P_n^* q(\lambda_n) S}{\sqrt{T_n^*}}$$

where

$$S = \sqrt{\left[k_g\left(\frac{2}{k_g+1}\right)^{(k_g+1)/(k_g-1)}\frac{g}{R_g}\right]}$$

If we substitute in the expression deduced above for R_{sp} (for $k_g = 1{\cdot}33$, and $R_g = 29{\cdot}5$, $S = 0{\cdot}388$) the expression obtained for G_a, we shall have

$$R_{sp} = \frac{\nu\sqrt{T_n^*}}{0{\cdot}388}\ \frac{[f(\lambda_n)\pi_n - 1]}{q(\lambda_n)\pi_n} - \frac{V}{g}$$

Comparing this equation with equation (1.17) we obtain[1]

$$R(\pi_n) = \frac{f(\lambda_n)\pi_n - 1}{\varphi_V\, 0{\cdot}388\, q(\lambda_n)\pi_n}. \qquad (1.19)$$

Equation (1.19) is just as applicable to a total expansion as to a convergent nozzle with a critical or higher pressure drop.

In the case of a convergent nozzle with a critical or higher pressure drop we have: $f(\lambda_n) = 1{\cdot}259$ (for $k_g = 1{\cdot}33$); $q(\lambda_n) = 1{\cdot}0$ and $\varphi_V = 1{\cdot}0$, if losses are taken into consideration in π_n via δ_c.

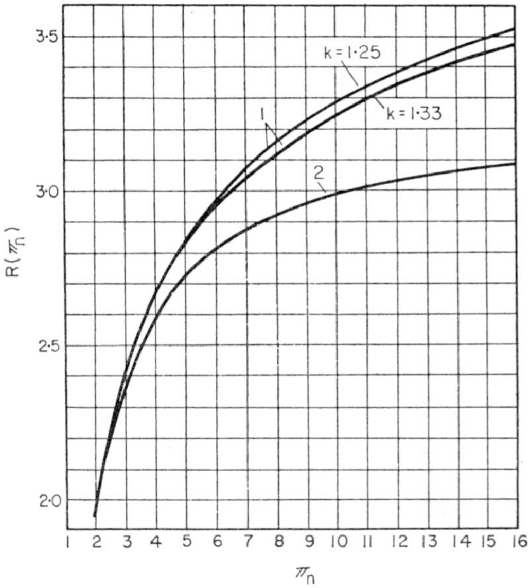

Fig. 1. Dependence of the function $R(\pi_n)$ on π_n.
(1) Full expansion; (2) Convergent nozzle.

[1] For this approximation, it is not taken into consideration that for a divergent nozzle the value of π_n according to equation (1.17) will be somewhat higher than according to equation (1.18), since in the latter case the losses in the divergent portion are also included in the value of π_n.

Consequently,

$$R(\pi_n) = \frac{1{\cdot}259\,\pi_n - 1}{0{\cdot}388\,\pi_n}\,. \tag{1.20}$$

For complete expansion, equation (1.15) will be used in future for determining $R\ (\pi_n)$.

Figure 1 shows the relationship $R\ (\pi_n) = f\ (\pi_n)$ for complete and incomplete expansion.

Equations for Specific Fuel Consumption

The efficiency of a turbo-jet engine is usually assessed by means of the specific fuel consumption, determined (in kg/kg thrust hr,) from the relationship

$$C_R = \frac{G_f}{R} \tag{1.21}$$

where G_f is the hourly fuel consumption in kg/hr.

It should be noted, that in such a form the specific fuel consumption represents the parameter which characterizes a turbo-jet engine simultaneously as a heat engine and a propulsive engine.

The efficiency of a turbo-jet engine as a heat engine can be evaluated by means of the brake horse power efficiency, represented by the ratio of the available kinetic energy to the heat utilized.

The available kinetic energy is determined by the formula

$$E = \frac{G_g c^2}{2g} + \frac{G_g V^2}{2g} - \frac{G_a V^2}{g}\,. \tag{1.22}$$

In this expression the first term defines the kinetic energy of the gas on discharging from the engine, the second term is the kinetic energy of the gas which the latter provides in participating in the total motion together with the engine, and the third term is the work done by the propulsive forces corresponding in magnitude to the change of impulse on entry into the engine.

The expression for the available kinetic energy is of a general nature. Taking $G_y = G_i$, we obtain the frequently used expression

$$E = \frac{G_g}{2g}\,(c^2 - V^2)\,.$$

Taking $G_a=0$, we obtain

$$E = \frac{G_g}{2g}(c^2 + V^2).$$

This formula is used in this form for liquid-fuel rocket engines.

If it be assumed that $G_g=G_a$ only in the second term, then we obtain

$$E = \frac{G_g c^2}{2g} - \frac{G_a V^2}{2g}.$$

Using expression (1.22), the brake horse power efficiency can be written in the form

$$\eta_e = A\frac{\frac{G_g}{2g}c^2 + \frac{G_g}{2g}V^2 - \frac{G_a}{g}V^2}{G_{a.c}qH_u}, \tag{1.23}$$

where q is the quantity of fuel supplied to 1 kg of air admitted to the combustion chamber;

H_u is the calorific value of the fuel.

Using the symbols introduced above, we obtain

$$\eta_e = A\frac{\nu\frac{c^2 + V^2}{2g} - \frac{V^2}{g}}{\delta_{\text{cool}}qH_u}. \tag{1.24}$$

The brake horse power efficiency takes into account all forms of losses of energy in the engine itself – thermal, aerodynamic and mechanical. Consequently, this efficiency determines the fraction of the heat equivalent to the increase in the kinetic energy of the gas stream in the engine, utilized for creating the reactive thrust.

The efficiency of a turbo-jet engine as a propulsive engine is evaluated as the so called flight or propulsion efficiency, represented by the ratio of the operative propulsive force to the available kinetic energy:

$$\eta_t = \frac{RV}{\frac{G_g}{2g}c^2 + \frac{G_g}{2g}V^2 - \frac{G_a V^2}{g}}. \tag{1.25}$$

For complete expansion, using the symbols assumed earlier, we obtain

$$\eta_t = \frac{2V(\nu c - V)}{\nu c^2 - V^2(2-\nu)}. \tag{1.26}$$

With $\nu = 1{\cdot}0$ we obtain the well-known formula

$$\eta_t = \frac{2}{1+(c/V)}.$$

With $\nu = \infty$ $(G_a = 0)$ we have

$$\eta_t = \frac{2(c/V)}{1+(c/V)^2},$$

i. e. the expression for the flight efficiency of a liquid-fuel rocket engine.

The product of the brake horse power efficiency and the flight efficiency gives the total efficiency as the ratio of the useful operative thrust to the heat utilized

$$\eta_t \eta_e = \eta_0 = \frac{ARV}{G_{a.c} q H_u}$$

or

$$\eta_0 = \frac{3600\,AV}{H_u C_R}. \tag{1.27}$$

Thus for example, for a flight velocity corresponding to $M_H = 2{\cdot}5$ for $T_g^* = 1350°K$ and $\pi_c^* = 4{\cdot}0$, the specific fuel consumption C_R in the absence of a reheat chamber is equal to 1·5 kg/kg thrust.hr and $\eta_0 = 0{\cdot}406$.

In the case of the use of a reheat chamber for the same conditions, in which the temperature of the gas $T_\Phi^* = 2000°K$, we have $C_R = 2{\cdot}1$ kg/kg thrust.hr and $\eta_0 = 0{\cdot}28$.

The flight efficiency of an engine without a reheat chamber and with a reheat chamber will be equal to 0·80 and 0·665 respectively and the brake horse power efficiency will be 0·508 and 0·42. Thus, for the conditions considered, the efficiency is adequately high.

With a reduction in the flight velocity, the efficiencies of gas-turbine engines are reduced. Thus for example, in an engine having $M = 0{\cdot}94$ (1000 km/hr), $\pi_c^* = 14$ and $T_g^* = 1000°K$ (cruising regime), the fuel consumption $C_R = 0{\cdot}93$ kg/kg thrust.hr.

These conditions correspond to $\eta_0 = 0{\cdot}243$, $\eta_t = 0{\cdot}577$ and $\eta_e = 0{\cdot}421$. Thus, notwithstanding the lower values of C_R, the efficiency of this engine is less than in the one considered above.

The example presented shows graphically that values of C_R do not permit a comparison to be made of the efficiency of engines operating at different flight velocities. Even in the case of identical flight velocities the value of C_R may appear as the criterion of the efficiency of different engines. Moreover, this parameter also permits the efficiency of an engine to be evaluated under standard conditions.

If the specific fuel consumption relates not to the thrust, but to the work accomplished by the propulsive force, then it will be expressed in kg fuel/kg — hr, and is a criterion which permits a comparison to be made of the efficiency of the engine, independent of the flight velocity:

$$C_e = \frac{G_f}{RV},$$

whence

$$RV = \frac{G_f}{C_e}.$$

and consequently

$$\eta_0 = \frac{AG_f}{G_{a.c} H_u q C_e} = 3600 \frac{A}{H_u C_e}.$$

For identical η_0, C_e will also be equal, although the flight velocities and also η_e and η_t may be different.

The use of C_e for gas-turbine engines is inconvenient, since for standard conditions this parameter is unsuitable.

The specific fuel consumption, related to the thrust of the engine, is the primary parameter for evaluating the efficiency of a turbo-jet engine, and therefore it is also taken as fundamental in the present work.

Let us write down equation (1.21) in the form

$$C_R = \frac{3600\, G_{a.c} q}{G_a R_{sp}} = \frac{3600\, \delta_{cool} q}{R_{sp}} = \frac{\delta_{cool} q_0}{R_{sp}} \quad (1.28)$$

where $q_0 = 3600\ q$.

We shall substitute

$$q_0 = B\,(T_g^* - T_c^*),$$

where

$$B = f\left(C_p,\ H_u,\ \eta_g,\ T_g^*,\ \frac{T_g^*}{T_c^*}\right);$$

T_c is the temperature of the air on entry into the combustion chamber.

The equation for the coefficient B is discussed in the next section.

Let us substitute the temperature of the air T_c^* by the temperature of the throttled flow T_H^* and $l(\pi_c^*)$. We obtain

$$q_0 = BT_H^* \left\{ \frac{T_g^*}{T_H^*} - [1 + l(\pi_c)] \right\}. \quad (1.29)$$

If we substitute expression (1.29) in equation (1.28), and R_{sp} we replace by means of equation (1.17), then expression (1.28) assumes the form

$$C_R = \frac{B\sqrt{(T_H^*)}\,\delta_{cool}\left\{\frac{T_g^*}{T_H^*} - [1 + l(\pi_c^*)]\right\}}{\nu\varphi_V \sqrt{\left(\frac{T_t^*}{T_H^*}\right)} R(\pi_n) - 1{\cdot}87\lambda_H}.$$

If we introduce the concept of reduced specific fuel consumption

$$C_{R_{red}} = \frac{C_R}{B\sqrt{(T_H^*)}}.$$

Denoting

$$\Phi(q) = \frac{T_g^*}{T_H^*} - [1 + l(\pi_c^*)],$$

we obtain

$$C_{R_{red}} = \frac{\delta_{cool}\Phi(q)}{\nu\varphi_V \sqrt{\left(\frac{T_t^*}{T_H^*}\right)} R(\pi_n) - 1{\cdot}87\lambda_H}. \quad (1.30)$$

In this form, the right-hand portion of the equation is independent in the explicit form of the flight altitude and is a function of the dimensionless quantities T_g^*/T_H^*, $l(\pi_c^*)$, λ_H, $\pi_n T_t^*/T_H$, the efficiencies and the loss coefficients. This equation is convenient for theoretical studies. In order to facilitate the calculations, the functions $\Phi(q)$ and $R(\pi_n)$ may be presented in tables and in graphs.

Derivation of the Equation for Determining the Quantity of Fuel Supplied per 1 kg of Air in the Main Combustion Chamber[1]

The quantity of fuel q, supplied, per 1 kg of air in the main combustion chamber, for different values of the gas and air temperature can be determined by Kirchhoff's equation.

It should be noted that for determining the heating effect of a reaction by Kirchhoff's law, the difference in the increase of the enthalpies of the initial reactants and final reaction products should be determined over the same temperature range for which are determined the heating effects of the reaction.

The initial reactants i.e. air and fuel, are admitted into the combustion chamber at a different temperature. As a consequence of this, a certain temperature T^*_{cx} should be assumed, obtained as a result of the mixing of the initial reactants, in the process of which preheating of the fuel will take place from the temperature T_t to T^*_{cx} as a result of its partial or complete vaporization, and the temperature of the air will be reduced from T^*_c to T^*_{cx}. In connection with the complexity of the determination of the temperature T^*_{cx} and, assuming also a relatively small quantity of fuel, we shall apply an approximation for the initial temperatures of the air and fuel.

We write down Kirchhoff's equation in the form

$$Q_{Tc} = Q_{T_0} + \delta J, \tag{1.31}$$

where Q_{Tc} is the quantity of heat released by the combustion of q kg of fuel at a temperature of entry into the combustion chamber of T_c;

Q_{T_0} is the same at the original temperature;

$\delta J = \Delta J_1 - \Delta J_2$;

ΔJ_1 is the change of enthalpy of the initial combustion reactants as a result of transition from the temperatures T^*_c and T_t to T_0;

ΔJ_2 is the change of enthalpy of the final combustion products as a result of transition from the temperature T^*_c to T_0.

[1] This section has been prepared jointly with Ya. T. Il'ichev.

Let us substitute the left-hand portion of equation (1.31) by the following expression:

$$Q_{Tc}=(1+q)\,c_{pg}^{T_g^*}T_g^*-(1+q)\,c_{pg}^{T_c^*}T_c^*,$$

where c_{pg} is the mean specific heat of the combustion products within the range $T=0$ to the temperature denoted by the superscript.

We express the quantity Q_{T_0} by

$$Q_{T_0}=\eta_g q H_u,$$

where η_g is the coefficient of completeness of combustion.

The quantities ΔJ_1 and ΔJ_2 in the developed form can be expressed in the following manner:

$$\Delta J_1=c_{pa}^{T_c^*}T_c^*+qc_{pf}^{T_f}T_f-c_{pa}^{T_0}T_0-qc_{pf}^{T_0}T_0,$$

where c_{pa} is the mean specific heat of the air;
c_{pf} is the mean specific heat of the fuel;
T_f is the temperature of the fuel admitted into the combustion chamber;

$$\Delta J_2=(1+q)\,c_{pg}^{T_c^*}T_c^*-(1+q)\,c_{pg}^{T_0}T_0.$$

Substituting the expressions for Q_{Tc}, Q_{T_0}, ΔJ_1 and ΔJ_2 in equation (1.31), we have

$$q=\frac{c_{pg}^{T_g^*}T_g^*-c_{pa}^{T_c^*}T_c^*+c_{pa}^{T_0}T_0-c_{pg}^{T_0}T_0}{\eta_g H_u-c_{pg}^{T_g^*}T_g^*+c_{pg}^{T_0}T_0+c_{pf}^{T_f}T_f-c_{pf}^{T_0}T_0}\,. \tag{1.32}$$

The use of equation (1.32) is associated with well-known difficulties and particularly with the fact that the temperature of the fuel entering into it is usually unknown. Therefore equation (1.32) must be simplified. Approximate equations can be obtained from equation (1.32) by using one or other simplifying assumptions. Thus for example, if it be assumed that the temperature of the fuel is equal to the temperature T_0, then we obtain Prof. V. V. Uvarov's equation[1]

$$q=\frac{c_{pg}^{T_g^*}T_g^*-c_{pg}^{T_0}T_0-c_{pa}^{T_c^*}T_c^*+c_{pa}^{T_0}T_0}{\eta_g H_u-c_{pg}^{T_g^*}T_g^*+c_{pg}^{T_0}T_0}\,. \tag{1.33}$$

[1] According to lectures by Prof. V. V. Uvarov in Moscow Technical College.

By assuming the temperature of the fuel equal to the temperature of the air and the specific heat of the fuel equal to the specific heat of the air, we obtain

$$q = \frac{c_{pg}^{T_g^*} T_g^* - c_{pg}^{T_0} T_0 - c_{pa}^{T_c^*} T_c^* + c_{pa}^{T_0} T_0}{\eta_g H_u - c_{pg}^{T_g^*} T_g^* + c_{pg}^{T_0} T_0} \cdot \qquad (1.34)$$

Assuming

$$c_{pg}^{T_0} = c_{pa}^{T_0}$$

and that

$$c_{pg}^{T_0} T_0 + c_{pt}^{T_t} T_t - c_{pt}^{T_0} T_0 = c_{pa}^{T_c^*} T_c^*,$$

we obtain an approximate equation, differing only slightly from the equation proposed by T. M. Mel'kumov[1],

$$q = \frac{c_{pg}^{T_g^*} T_g^* - c_{pa}^{T_c^*} T_c^*}{\eta_g H_u - c_{pg}^{T_c^*} T_c^* + c_{pa}^{T_c^*} T_c^*} \cdot \qquad (1.35)$$

The following approximate equation of thermal balance is further expanded

$$q = \frac{c_{pg}^{T^*} T_g^* - c_{pg}^{T_c^*} T_c^*}{\eta_g H_u - c_{pg}^{T_g^*} T_g^* + c_{pg}^{T_c^*} T_c^*} \cdot \qquad (1.36)$$

This equation is obtained as a result of the following assumptions

$$c_{pg}^{T_0} T_0 + c_{pa}^{T_c^*} T_c^* - c_{pa}^{T_0} T_0 = c_{pg}^{T_c^*} T_c^*,$$

and also $\quad c_{pt}^{T_t^*} T_t^* = c_{pg}^{T_c^*} T_c^*$ and $c_{pt}^{T_0} = c_{pg}^{T_0}$.

Finally, it can be shown that the equation used is of the following form:

$$q = \frac{c_{pg}^{T^*} T_g^* - c_{pg}^{T_c^*} T_c^*}{\eta_g H_u} \cdot \qquad (1.37)$$

This equation can be derived, if, in addition to the equation

$$c_{pg}^{T_0} T_0 + c_{pa}^{T_c^*} T_c^* - c_{pa}^{T_c^*} T_0 = c_{pg}^{T_c^*} T_c^*,$$

it is assumed that

$$c_{pg}^{T_g^*} T_g^* - c_{pg}^{T_0} T_0 = c_{pt}^{T_t} T_t - c_{pt}^{T_0} T_0.$$

[1] T. M. Mel'kumov, *Teoriya Bystrokhodnovo Dvigatelya s Samovosplameneniem (Theory of High-speed Engines with Auto ignition)*, Oborongiz, 1953.

An analysis of the various equations derived for the conditions $\eta_g=0{\cdot}98$, $T_0=288°K$, $C_{p_t}=0{\cdot}5$, and for several values of the fuel temperature, has shown that the greatest deviation from the values obtained according to the original equation is given by Formula (1.37) and the least (up to 0·3 per cent) by Formula (1.33).

Formula (1.36) gives a deviation amounting to 3·5 per cent. Of the remaining formulae used for determining the fuel consumption, the least deviation (up to 1·5 per cent) is given by equation (1·35).

If Formula (1.33) is taken as the basic formula, q can be determined analytically or graphically. The latter is the most convenient.

In Fig. 2, a graph is shown for determining $q_0=3600q$ over a range of temperature of the gas from 900 to 1200°K. The values of

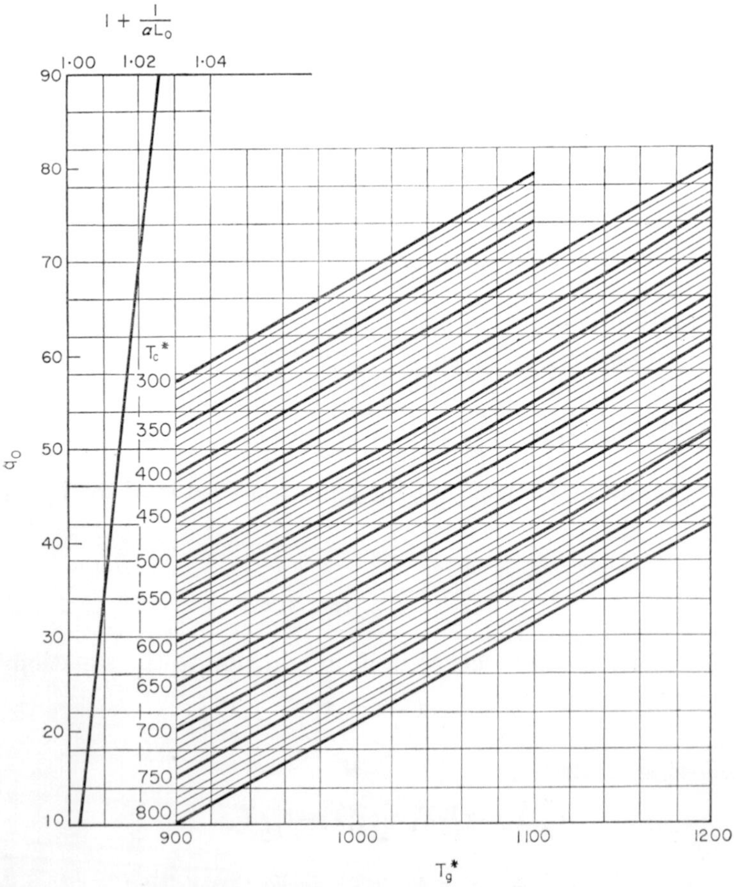

Fig. 2. Determination of q_0.

q are computed according to Formula (1.33) as a result of using the specific heats according to data by M. P. Vukalovich,[1] converted to the absolute scale.

It was also assumed for the calculations that $H_u = 10{,}250$ cal/kg and $\eta_g = 0{\cdot}97$.

In the case of another value for η_g it can be assumed, with a high degree of accuracy, that

$$q_{0x} = q_0 \frac{0{\cdot}97}{\eta_{gx}},$$

where q_{0x} corresponds to η_{gx}.

The conversion for another value of H_u is carried out similarly. For an analytical study of a turbo-jet engine, it is inconvenient to use the quantity q_0 directly. In connection with this, it was proposed earlier to write the expression for q_0 in the form

$$q_0 = B\,(T_g^* - T_c^*).$$

Here

$$B = 3600 \frac{q}{T_g^* - T_c^*}.$$

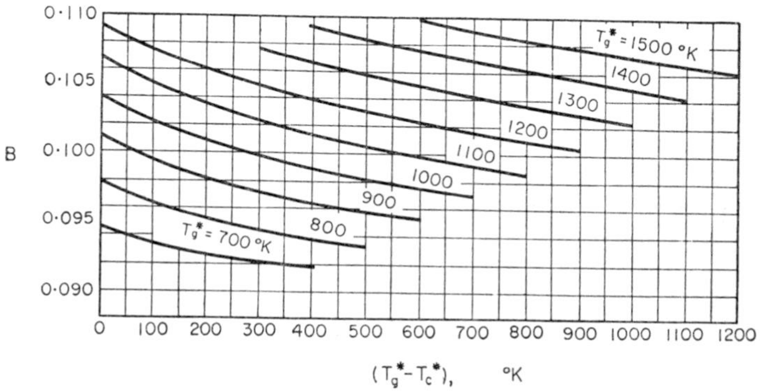

Fig. 3. Determination of the coefficient B.

In Fig. 3 a graph is shown for determining the coefficient B as a function of $(T_g^* - T_c^*)$ for different values of T_g^*. The quantity q has similarly been computed as for the graph shown in Fig. 2.

[1] Vukalovich M. P., Kirillin V. A. *et al*, *Termodinamicheskie Svoistva Gazov (Thermodynamic Properties of Gases)*, Mashgiz, 1953.

In the case of change of η_g, the coefficient B, as also q, can be converted according to the formula

$$B_x = B\frac{0{\cdot}97}{\eta_{gx}}.$$

It can be seen from Fig. 3 that for average values of T_g^* and $(T_g^*-T_c^*)$ the coefficient $B=0{\cdot}102-0{\cdot}104$. For $T_g^*=T_c^*$ the quantity $q=0$ and the formula for B leads to the indeterminate form 0/0.

Solving this indeterminancy by the usual method, by assuming $T_g=$const., we obtain

$$B_{T_g^*\to T_c^*} = \frac{3600}{c}\left[c_{pa}^{T_c^*} + T_c^*\left(\frac{\mathrm{d}c_{pa}}{\mathrm{d}T_c^*}+\frac{\mathrm{d}c_{pg}}{\mathrm{d}T_c^*}\right) - T\,\frac{\mathrm{d}c_{pg}}{\mathrm{d}T_c^*}\right], \quad (1.38)$$

where

$$c=\eta_g H_u-(c_{pg}^{T_g^*}T_g^*-c_{pg}^{T_0}T_0).$$

The derivatives entering into equation (1.38) should be determined by the graphical differentiation of the curves $c_p=f(T)$. As a result of this the derivatives $\mathrm{d}c_{pg}/\mathrm{d}T_c^*$ should be determined according to the graph of the specific heats of the gas at constant temperature T_g^* for variable values of T_c^*, i.e. for various values of α.

Values of B are given in Fig. 3, calculated according to equation (1.38) for $T_g^*-T_c^*=0$.

2. Optimum Thermodynamic Parameters of Turbo-jet Engines

General Data concerning Thermodynamic Parameters guaranteeing Minimum Specific Fuel Consumption

The specific fuel consumption C_R is a function of many variables. In a general form, the expression for C_R can be written down by the following functional equation:

$$C_R=f(\pi_c^*,\,T_g^*,\,T_H^*,\,\lambda_H,\,\eta_c^*,\,\eta_t^*,\,\delta_i,\,\delta_c,\,\delta_g,\,\varphi_v,\,a,\,B). \quad (1.39)$$

If it be assumed that all the variables are independent, then, as is well known, the minimum for a function of many variables should be attained only for those values of independent variables for which the partial derivatives of C_R vanish or do not exist. If the partial derivatives exist, then, by equating them to zero, we obtain a system of equations from which those values of the independent variables are determined, for which the function may attain a maximum or a minimum.

For a complete solution to the problem it is further necessary to carry out an analysis of the values obtained, for which, in order to verify it, either the function does in fact attain a maximum or a minimum for these values of the independent variables.

It should be noted that the dependence of C_R on all the calculated variables is continuous, excluding a few limiting points, and the partial derivatives exist.

However, the partial derivatives of C_R with respect to η_c^*, η_t^* δ_t, and other coefficients, which take losses into consideration i.e. $\partial C_R/\partial \eta_c^*$; $\partial C_R/\partial \eta_t^*$ etc, do not vanish, since it is obvious that the larger these coefficients, the less is the value of C_R, and for approximately the same conditions the least physically possible specific fuel consumption will be achieved when one or other of the coefficients mentioned, or all the coefficients are equal to unity.

The partial derivatives $\partial C_R/\partial \lambda_H$ and $\partial C_R/\partial T_H$ similarly do not vanish, since with a decrease in λ_H and T_H the value of C_R is monotonically reduced, which can be seen, for example, from Formula (1.30).

The required limit for λ_H is equal to zero, and for T_H it is the physically possible minimum temperature under high altitude or terrestrial conditions.

The coefficient B cannot appear as an independent variable, since the specific heat depends on the temperature of the gas and on the temperature of the air on entry into the combustion chamber, or as a result of fixing λ_H, T_H and η_c^* – from T_g^* and π_c^*.

Two equations can be written down for determining the minimum C_R taking into account what has been stated above

$$\left.\begin{aligned}\frac{\partial C_R}{\partial \pi_c^*} &= \left(\frac{\partial C_R}{\partial \pi_c}\right) + \frac{\partial C_R}{\partial B}\frac{\partial B}{\partial \pi_c^*} = 0\,;\\ \frac{\partial C_R}{\partial T_g^*} &= \left(\frac{\partial C_R}{\partial T_g^*}\right) + \frac{\partial C_R}{\partial B}\frac{\partial B}{\partial T_g^*} = 0\,.\end{aligned}\right\} \tag{1.40}$$

where $\left(\frac{\partial C_R}{\partial \pi_c^*}\right)$ and $\left(\frac{\partial C_R}{\partial T_g}\right)$ are the partial derivatives of C_R, evaluated directly with respect to π_c^* and to T_g^*.

By solving the system of equations (1.40), all the remaining variables should be fixed by some values, which, in a particular case, may also be the limiting values with respect to size. If, for the purposes of simplification, the coefficient B is assumed to be constant, then the system of equations (1.40) takes the form

$$\left(\frac{\partial C_R}{\partial \pi_c^*}\right) = 0\,, \quad \left(\frac{\partial C_R}{\partial T_g^*}\right) = 0\,. \tag{1.41}$$

In future presentations the brackets will be omitted.

The condition that $B=\text{const.}$ is, in practice, equivalent to constant specific heat and constant values of H_u and η_g, since the effect of the difference $C_{pg}\ (T_g^* - T_0)$ in the substituted equation (1.33) is small.

Each one of the equations in the system (1.41) has a separate solution in the general case. Further, the simultaneous solution of these equations, as was shown above, only exists for certain conditions.

However, in an ideal engine (without thermal and aerodynamic losses) the partial derivatives of C_R, just as with respect to π_c^* so also with respect to T_g^* cannot be equal to zero, since the fuel consumption will be monotonically reduced according to the extent of reduction in the temperature of the gas as a result of fixing π_c^*, or as a result of increasing π_c^* in the case when $T_g^*=\text{const.}$

In a real engine, with reduction in the supply of heat (on account of the reduction of T_g^* for $\pi_c^*=\text{const.}$, or an increase in π_c^* for $T_g^*=\text{const.}$), the specific fuel consumption is first of all reduced, attains a minimum value and then increases. This change of the specific fuel consumption is a characteristic property of a turbo-jet engine and is explained by the fact that the efficiency of the engine is assessed according to the fuel consumption, related to the thrust.

If in a turbo-jet engine the fuel consumption be related not to the thrust but to the performance cycle, as is accepted in piston engines and in internal combustion engines, then as a result of the reduction in the supply of heat the efficiency of a turbo-jet engine should deteriorate continuously.

Let us consider this problem, taking the flow rate of air through the engine as $G_a=1$ kg/sec and neglecting the difference between the flow rates of air and gas. The performance cycle in this case will be determined by the available kinetic energy of the gas, i. e.,

$$E_0 = \frac{c^2}{2g} - \frac{V^2}{2g}.$$

The specific fuel consumption is

$$C_e = 3600 \frac{q}{E_0}.$$

On the other hand, the available kinetic energy can be written in the following manner;

$$AE_0 = qH_u - AL_R,$$

where AL_R is the internal thermal, aerodynamic and mechanical move up losses of energy in the engine.

The overwhelming portion of the internal losses consist of the loss of heat contained in the exhaust gases

$$Q_B = A \frac{k_g}{k_g - 1} R_g (T_n - T_H) \quad .$$

Q_B takes into account all the losses with respect to the engine duct, excluding the losses from incompleteness of combustion and mechanical losses.

Using the expression for E_0, we obtain

$$C_e = 3600 \frac{Aq}{(qH_u - AL_R)} = 3600 \frac{A}{H_u\left(1 - \frac{AL_R}{qH_u}\right)}. \tag{1.42}$$

According to the extent of the reduction of the heat supply qH_u for a constant value of L_R, the specific fuel consumption should be increased, which corresponds simultaneously to a reduction in the brake horse power efficiency

$$\eta_e = \frac{AE_0}{qH_u} = 3600 \frac{A}{H_u C_e}. \tag{1.43}$$

When $qH_u \rightarrow AL_R$, then $C_e \rightarrow \infty$ and $\eta_e \rightarrow 0$.

If $qH_u \rightarrow \infty$, then $C_e = 3600 \dfrac{A}{H_u}$ and $\eta_e \rightarrow 1{\cdot}0$.

If the propulsive specific fuel consumption be considered for the same conditions, then we shall have

$$C_R = 3600 \frac{q}{R_{sp}}.$$

Let us introduce the quantity E, connected with E_0 by the relationship

$$E = E_0 + \frac{V^2}{2g} = \frac{c^2}{2g}.$$

Then

$$c = \sqrt{(2gE)}, \quad R_{sp} = \frac{1}{g}(\sqrt{(2gE)} - V).$$

On the other hand

$$E = \frac{qH_u}{A} - L_R + \frac{V^2}{2g}.$$

Therefore, the specific fuel consumption is expressed by the equation

$$C_R = \frac{3600q}{\frac{1}{g}\left[\sqrt{\left\{2g\left(\frac{qH_u}{A} - L_R + \frac{V^2}{2g}\right)\right\}} - V\right]}. \tag{1.44}$$

In this equation, as distinct from equation (1.42), C may either be increased or decreased as a result of a reduction in q. For $qH_u = AL_R$, $C_R = \infty$. If further $q = \infty$, then, removing the indeterminancy ∞/∞, we likewise obtain $C_R = \infty$. Consequently, in the interval between the stated values of q there exists such a value of it for which $\partial C_R/\partial q = 0$ and the specific fuel consumption is a minimum.

Taking the derivative of C_R with respect to q and equating it to zero, we obtain, after transformation, a simple equation for determining q, for which the specific fuel consumption has a minimum value. Let us carry out briefly the derivation of this equation.

After differentiating equation (1.44), we obtain

$$\left[\sqrt{\left\{2g\left(\frac{qH_u}{A} - L_R + \frac{V^2}{2g}\right)\right\}} - V\right] - q\frac{2g\frac{H_u}{A}}{2\sqrt{\left[2g\frac{qH_u}{A} - L_R + \frac{V^2}{2g}\right]}} = 0$$

or

$$2g\left(\frac{qH_u}{A} - L_R + \frac{V^2}{2g}\right) - V\sqrt{\left[2g\left(\frac{qH_u}{A} - L_R + \frac{V^2}{2g}\right)\right]} - g\frac{qH_u}{A} = 0 .$$

We designate

$$x = \sqrt{\left[2g\left(\frac{qH_u}{A} - L_R + \frac{V^2}{2g}\right)\right]}.$$

Then the previous equation takes the form

$$x^2 - Vx - g\frac{qH_u}{A} = 0,$$

whence, taking only the positive solution, we have:

$$x = \frac{V}{2} + \sqrt{\left(\frac{V^2}{4} + g\frac{qH_u}{A}\right)}.$$

Consequently,

$$2g\left(\frac{qH_u}{A} - L_R + \frac{V^2}{2g}\right) = \frac{V^2}{4} + V\sqrt{\left(\frac{V^2}{4} + g\frac{qH_u}{A}\right)} + \frac{V^2}{4} + g\frac{qH_u}{A}.$$

After reducing like terms we have

$$g\cdot\frac{qH_u}{A} - 2gL_R + \frac{V^2}{2} = V\sqrt{\left(\frac{V^2}{4} + g\frac{qH_u}{A}\right)}.$$

Squaring both sides of this equation and carrying out cancellations, we obtain

$$\left(\frac{qH_u}{A}\right)^2 - 4\frac{qH_u}{A}L_R + (2L_R)^2 - 2L_R\frac{V^2}{g} = 0.$$

We solve this equation relative to qH_u/A:

$$\frac{q_{\text{opt}}H_u}{AL_R} = 2\left(1 + \sqrt{\left\{\frac{V^2}{2gL_R}\right\}}\right) \quad (1.45)$$

Consequently,

$$C_{R_{\min}} = \frac{3600\cdot 2g\frac{AL_R}{H_u}\left(1 + \sqrt{\left\{\frac{V^2}{2gL_R}\right\}}\right)}{\sqrt{\left[2gL_R\left(1 + \frac{V^2}{2gL_R} + \sqrt{\left\{2\frac{V^2}{gL_R}\right\}}\right) - V\right.}} \quad (1.46)$$

In the special case for $V = 0$

$$\frac{q_{\text{opt}}H_u}{AL_R} = 2{\cdot}0 \quad (1.47)$$

and

$$C_{R_{\min}} = 3600\frac{A}{H_u}\sqrt{(2gL_R)} \quad (1.48)$$

or

$$C_{R_{\min}} = 3600\sqrt{\left(\frac{gA}{H_u}q_{\text{opt}}\right)} \quad (1.49)$$

The equation obtained for q_{opt} clearly shows that the conditions for which the minimum fuel consumption is achieved are determined only by the ratios of the losses in the cycle and the heat supply on the one hand, and the kinetic energy corresponding to the flight velocity on the other hand. In particular, it is expedient to note the following:

1. With increase of the losses, q_{opt} also increases, i.e. the optimum temperature of the gas should be increased for a given expansion ratio, or the optimum value of π_c^* should be increased for a given T_g^*.

2. With increase of flight velocity, q_{opt} also increases and consequently, $T_{g.\text{opt}}$ or $\pi^*_{c\ \text{opt}}$ should be correspondingly changed. For a given L_R the least value of q_{opt} is obtained for $V=0$.

The brake horse power efficiency corresponding to q and $C_{R.\,\text{min}}$ also increases with increase of flight velocity. From equation (1.24), for $\nu=1$ and $\delta_{\text{cool}}=1$ after substituting

$$\frac{c^2-V^2}{2g}=\frac{qH_u}{A}-L_R$$

we obtain

$$\eta_e=\left(1-\frac{AL_R}{qH_u}\right).$$

Substituting in place of q the expression for q_{opt} we obtain

$$\eta_{eq=q_{\text{opt}}}=1-\frac{1}{2\left(1+\sqrt{\left\{\dfrac{V^2}{2gL_R}\right\}}\right)}.$$

For $V\to\infty$, $\eta_e=q_{\text{opt}}\to 1{\cdot}0$.

If $V=0$, then $\eta_{eq}=q_{\text{opt}}=0{\cdot}5$.

It is very characteristic that for $V=0$, the maximum brake horse power efficiency of a turbo-jet engine $\eta_e=0{\cdot}5$ is independent of the absolute value of qH_u and AL_R. It is only necessary that qH_u should be twice as great as AL_R (see equation 1.47). This situation has not been recorded previously in the literature.

It will be shown below that the maximum value of $\eta_e=0{\cdot}5$, corresponding to the optimum value of q for $V=0$ is achieved at extremely high values of the expansion ratio and of the gas temperature. It is well-known that for modern turbo-jet engines under standard conditions $\eta_e=0{\cdot}25-0{\cdot}35$.

3. The flight altitude in an explicit form does not enter into equations (1.5) and (1.6) and, consequently, for given values of L_R and V just as for q_{opt} so also the minimum specific fuel consumption for change of flight altitude should not be changed.

If, further, the main possibility is taken into account, of increase of L_R because of reduction of the Reynold's number with increase of altitude, then the values of q_{opt} and $C_{R_{\text{min}}}$ may even be increased. It can be shown that this situation contradicts what has been said above concerning the effect of T_H on C_R. and also contradicts well-known data, in accordance with which the magnitude of $C_{R_{\text{min}}}$ is reduced with increase of altitude.

Such a discrepancy is a consequence of the fact that the comparison of $C_{R_{\text{min}}}$ is usually carried out at different altitudes with a constant expansion ratio, constant values of the efficiencies and of the pressure coefficients. In this case, with increase of altitude the work expended on the compressor is reduced, which leads to a reduction of the magnitude of the losses in the compressor and in the turbine.

If the comparison is carried out for identical work expended on the compressor and with constant η_c^*, then with increase in flight altitude the losses in the cycle will be reduced, as a consequence of the increase of the expansion ratio and, consequently, in this case q_{opt} and $C_{R_{\text{min}}}$ will be reduced.

Further, when the condition $L_R = \text{const.}$ is superimposed, then the reduction of the losses on account of the increase in π_c^*, or the reduction of the work expended on the compressor, should be compensated by an increase in the other losses in the cycle, as a consequence of which the flight altitude will not have an effect on $C_{R_{\text{min}}}$.

Conditions for obtaining Minimum C_R as a Function of the Two Variables π_c^* and T_g^*

The method of investigating C_R by means of the quantity q and the total losses in the cycle can be applied for considering the problem of the simultaneous of the system of equations (1.41) and, consequently, for determining whether C_R can have a minimum simultaneously with respect to the two variables π_c^* and T_g^*. This problem has not been discussed previously in the literature. It follows from general theory concerning the maximum and minimum function of two variables, that in order to obtain a minimum

C_R with respect to π_c^* and with respect to T_g^*, the following conditions should be observed:

$$\frac{\partial^2 C_R}{\partial T_g^{*2}} \frac{\partial^2 C_R}{\partial \pi_c^{*2}} - \left(\frac{\partial^2 C_R}{\partial T_g^* \partial \pi_c^*}\right)^2 > 0 \text{ and } \frac{\partial^2 C_R}{\partial T_g^{*2}} > 0 .$$

Because of the complexity of the expression for C_R, an investigation by means of these conditions is practically impossible. Therefore, we shall adopt the more simple method of taking into consideration the physical processes in the engine.

It was shown above that the quantity q is, primarily, a function of the gas temperature T_g^* and of the temperature of the air on entry into the combustion chamber T_c^*, if it be assumed that η_g H_u and T_0 are constant quantities. If, in addition, the altitude and, velocity of flight are given and $\eta_c^* = \text{const.}$ then we can write down

$$q = f\,(T_g^*;\ \pi_c^*).$$

We shall suppose, as we did previously, that $L_R = \text{const.}$ and therefore the specific fuel consumption is a function only of q, i. e. $C_R = f\,(q)$; then

$$\frac{\partial C_R}{\partial T_g^*} = \frac{\partial C_R}{\partial q} \frac{\partial q}{\partial T_g^*} ,$$

and

$$\frac{\partial C_R}{\partial \pi_c^*} = \frac{\partial C_R}{\partial q} \frac{\partial q}{\partial \pi_c^*} .$$

Since for the minimum value of C_R the derivative $\frac{\partial C_R}{\partial q} = 0$, we obtain

$$\frac{\partial C_R}{\partial T_g^*} = 0 \text{ and } \frac{\partial C_R}{\partial \pi_c^*} = 0.$$

Therefore the minimum value of C_R with respect to q (for $L_R = \text{const}$) is simultaneously a minimum with respect to π_c^* and T_g^* and, consequently, the values of these quantities, which correspond to the optimum value of q, are also optima.

Since the result obtained holds good only in the case when the quantity L_R is assumed to be constant, then, consequently, the quantities π_c^* and T_g^* will be obtained by this condition. It is also obvious that they will further depend on the assumed efficiency level of the units.

Figure 4 shows the function $C_R=f\,(qH_u)$. The value of $AL_R=$ $=140$ cal/kg corresponds to an engine with a centrifugal compressor. The initial value of C_R and qH_u is marked on this curve by the point 0 and corresponds to $\pi_c^*=4{\cdot}5$, $T_g^*=1100$°K, $qH_u=175$ cal/kg for $\eta_c^*=0{\cdot}778$, $\eta_t^*=0{\cdot}876$ and $\delta_\Sigma=0{\cdot}88$.

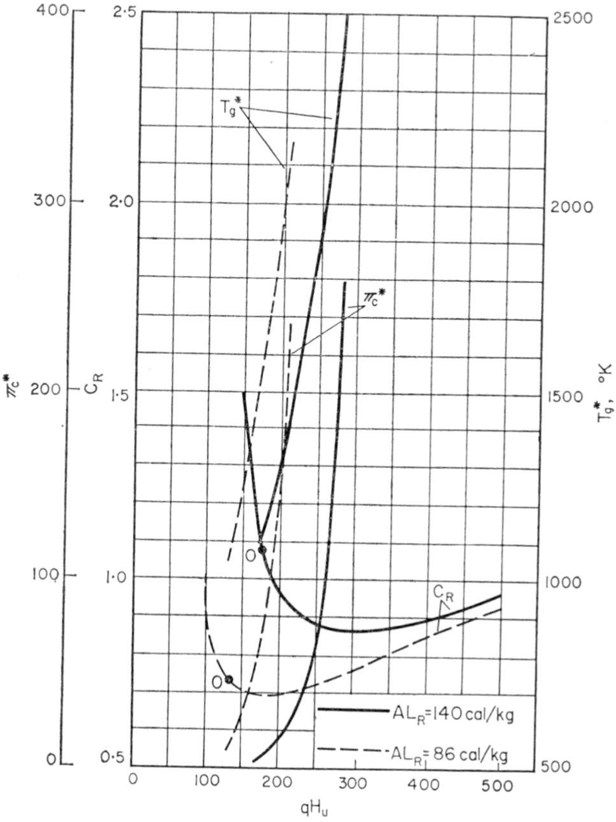

Fig. 4. Dependence of C_R, π_c^* and T_g^* on qH_u for $M=0$ and $H=0$.

In order to obtain minimum specific fuel consumption for $AL_R=$ $=140$ cal/kg it is necessary to increase qH_u from 175 to 280 cal/kg, which is associated with an increase of temperature of the gas prior to the turbine and with the expansion ratio. This can be seen from the curves drawn in Fig. 4, which show the variation of π_c^* and T_g^* for constant values of the efficiency. At the point of minimum C_R the expansion ratio and the temperature of the gas attain extremely high, unreal values ($\pi_c^*=257$, $T_g^*=2500$°K).

If it be assumed that at the point of minimum C_R the efficiency has a higher value (for example, $\pi_{kc}^*=0{\cdot}85$, $\eta_t^*=0{\cdot}92$, and $\delta_\Sigma= =0{\cdot}92$), then the optimum values of π_c^* and T_g^* are reduced to $T_g^*=1875$°K and $\pi_c^*=62$, which are also extremely large. For these efficiencies and values of π_c^* and T_g^* appropriate for modern gas-turbine engines, a relatively small value of AL_R can be obtained. In particular, for $\pi_c^*=11{\cdot}5$ and $T_g^*=1100$°K we obtain $AL_R = = 86$ cal/kg. The specific fuel consumption in this case (point 0′ in Fig. 4) is equal to 0·72 kg/kg thrust.hr and only differs slightly from the minimum, which is equal to 0·7 kg/kg thrust.hr.

It is very characteristic, however, that in order to obtain $C_{R\min}= =0{\cdot}7$ it is necessary to increase π_c^* (up to ~ 63) and T_g^* (up to $\sim$ 1580°K) considerably.

Thus, except for $L_R=$const., there is a minimum specific fuel consumption corresponding simultaneously to the optimum values of π_c^* and T_g^*, but these parameters, however, should have extremely large, practically unreal numerical values.

Since in the case considered π_c^* and T_g^* were connected together by the supplementary condition that $L_R=$const., then the so called relative minimum C_R was obtained with respect to the two variables.

If the temperature of the gas and the expansion ratio were varied independently, then L_R will be a variable quantity. Therefore, for constant efficiencies we can write:

$$C_R=f_1\,(q;\ L_R);$$
$$q\ =f_2\,(T_g^*;\ \pi_c^*);$$
$$L_R=f_3\,(T_g^*;\ \pi_c^*).$$

The partial derivatives of C_R, as a complex function with respect to the independent variables π_c^* and T_g^* are expressed by the equations

$$\frac{\partial C_R}{\partial T_g^*}=\frac{\partial C_R}{\partial q}\,\frac{\partial q}{\partial T_g^*}+\frac{\partial C_R}{\partial L_R}\,\frac{\partial L_R}{\partial T_g^*};$$

$$\frac{\partial C_R}{\partial \pi_c^*}=\frac{\partial C_R}{\partial q}\,\frac{\partial q}{\partial \pi_c^*}+\frac{\partial C_R}{\partial L_R}\,\frac{\partial L_R}{\partial \pi_c^*}.$$

In order that the partial derivatives of C_R with respect to T_g^* and with respect to π_c^* should, in this case, be simultaneously equal to zero, it is necessary that one of the following two conditions should be observed:

$$\frac{\partial C_R}{\partial q}=0 \text{ and } \frac{\partial C_R}{\partial L_R}=0$$

or

$$\frac{\partial q}{\partial T_g^*}\,\frac{\partial L_R}{\partial \pi_c^*}=\frac{\partial q}{\partial \pi_c^*}\,\frac{\partial L_R}{\partial T_g^*}.$$

It has already been mentioned above that the partial derivative $\partial C_R/\partial q$ can be equal to zero and this corresponds to minimum C_R with respect to π_c^* and with respect to T_g^* for $L_R=$ const. However, the existence of the equation $\partial C_R/\partial L_R=0$, within the limits of actual values of q, is impossible, which can easily be shown by considering for simplicity the case when the flight velocity is equal to zero.

For this case, by differentiating equation (1.44) we obtain

$$\frac{\partial C_R}{\partial L_R}=386\,\frac{Aq}{2(qH_u-AL_R)^{3/2}}=386\,\frac{A}{2q^{1/2}\left(H_u-\dfrac{AL_R}{q}\right)^{3/2}}.$$

It follows from this expression that dC_R/dL_R can be equal to zero only in the physically unreal case when $q=\infty$.

Thus, the first condition for the existence of a minimum C_R with respect to the two variables (π_c^* and T_g^*) for $L_R\neq$ const., cannot be fulfilled.

Let us consider the second condition.

For simplicity we shall assume that in the expression for q, the coefficient $B=$const. Then, for $T_H=$const. we obtain $dq/dT_g^*=B$ and

$$\frac{dq}{d\pi_c^*}=-BT_H l(\pi_c^*)'=-BT_H^*{}^{(k-1)/k}\frac{1}{\pi_c^{*1/k}\eta_c^*}.$$

Therefore, the second condition can be written in the form

$$\frac{dL_R}{d\pi_c^*}+T_H^*{}^{(k-1)/k}\frac{1}{\pi_c^{*1/k}\eta_c^*}\,\frac{dL_R}{dT_g^*}=0. \tag{1.50}$$

We shall express L_R as the sum of the losses in an ideal cycle and the losses from imperfection of the units of the engine:

$$L_R=L_{Ri}+L_R^{\mathrm{I}}+L_R^{\mathrm{II}}+L_R^{\mathrm{III}}+\ldots,$$

where L_{Ri} represents the losses in an ideal cycle;
$L_R^{I}, L_R^{II}, \ldots$ are the losses from imperfection of the engine units (compressor, combustion chamber, etc.).

Then equation (1.50) can be given in the form

$$\left(\frac{dL_{Ri}}{d\pi_c^*}+e\frac{dL_{Ri}}{dT_g^*}\right)+\left(\frac{dL_R^{I}}{d\pi_c^*}+e\frac{dL_R^{I}}{dT_g^*}\right)+\left(\frac{dL_R^{II}}{d\pi_c^*}+e\frac{dL_R^{II}}{dT_g^*}\right)+\ldots=0 \qquad (1.51)$$

where

$$e=T_H^{*(k-1)/k}\frac{1}{\pi_c^{*1/k}\eta_c^*}.$$

Let us consider firstly the conditions for which this equation holds good in an ideal cycle, i.e. when losses in the engine units are absent. The quantity L_{Ri} is expressed by the formula

$$L_{Ri}=\frac{H_u q}{A}(1-\eta_t).$$

Here η_t is the thermal efficiency of the cycle

$$\eta_t=1-\frac{1}{\pi_c^{*(k_0-1)/k_0}}$$

where k_0 is the average exponent of the cycle.

Differentiating the equation presented above, we obtain

$$\frac{\partial L_{Ri}}{\partial\pi_c^*}=-\frac{H_u}{A}B(1-\eta_t)e-\frac{H_u}{A}q\frac{(k_0-1)/k_0}{\pi_c^{*(2k_0-1)/k_0}};$$

$$\frac{\partial L_{Ri}}{\partial T_g^*}=\frac{H_u}{A}B(1-\eta_t);\ e\frac{\partial L_{Ri}}{\partial T_g^*}-\frac{H_u}{A}B(1-\eta_t)e.$$

Substituting in equation (1.51) the expressions obtained and assuming that the losses L_R^{I}, L_R^{II}, etc., are equal to zero, we obtain

$$-\frac{H_u}{A}\frac{k_0-1}{k_0}\frac{q}{\pi_c^{*(2k_0-1)/k_0}}=0$$

or

$$q=0.$$

Thus, for an ideal cycle the differential equation (1.51) is satisfied only in the limiting case for $q=0$. For this the temperature of the gas and the expansion ratio will be connected by the relationship

$$T_g^*=T_H^*\,[1+l\,(\pi_c^*)].$$

When $\pi_c^*=1{\cdot}0$, then $T_g^*=T_H^*$.
If $\pi_c^*\to\infty$, then also $T_g^*\to\infty$.

Consequently, in an ideal cycle π_c^* and T_g^* can have a wide range of values satisfying equation (1.51) from $\pi_c^*=1{\cdot}0$ and $T_g^*=$ $=T_H^*$ to $\pi_c^*=\infty$ and $T_g^*=\infty$. In the latter case and for an ideal cycle, all the terms of equation (1.51) should be equal to zero, since the thermal efficiency of the cycle is $\eta_t^*\to1{\cdot}0$, and the derivative of the losses in the engine units is $L_R^{\mathrm{I}}=L_R^{\mathrm{II}}\ \ldots\ \to0$. Thus, the conditions that $\pi_c^*=\infty$ and $T_g^*=\infty$ are solutions to equation (1.51), just as for an ideal cycle so also for an actual cycle. However, in an actual cycle this equation may have a solution for finite values of π_c^* and T_g^*, since the terms of equation (1.51) containing derivatives of the losses, increase according to the extent of the reduction in efficiency and may become commensurable with the first term for finite values of π_c^* and T_g^*, having, as a result of this, different signs.

In order to show this, we shall consider some of the losses and their partial derivatives, making use of the expressions for these losses obtained by A. L. Parkhomov. In particular, for the compressor

$$L_R^{\mathrm{I}}=\frac{H_{\mathrm{ad.}c}(1-\pi_c^*)}{\pi_c^{*(k_g-1)/k_g}\eta_c^*}.$$

Differentiating, we obtain

$$\frac{\partial L_R^{\mathrm{II}}}{\partial T_g^*}=0;$$

$$\frac{\partial R_L^{\mathrm{II}}}{\partial\pi_c^*}=\frac{\frac{k}{k-1}RT_H(1-\eta_c^*)}{\eta_c^*}\,\frac{\frac{k-1}{k}\,\frac{\pi_c^{*(k_g-1)/k_g}}{\pi_c^{*1/k}}-\frac{k_g-1}{k_g}\,\frac{\pi_c^{*(k-1)/k}-1}{\pi_c^{*1/k_g}}}{\pi_c^{*(2k_g-1)/k_g}}$$

If the difference between k_g and k be neglected, then we obtain

$$\frac{\partial L_R^{\mathrm{I}}}{\partial\pi_c^*}=\frac{RT_H^*(1-\eta_c^*)}{\eta_c^*}\,\frac{1}{\pi_c^{*2(k-1)/k}}.$$

When π_c^* increases beyond all bounds, then $\partial L_R^{\mathrm{I}}/\partial\pi_c^*\to0$. However, for an increase of efficiency the derivative $\partial L_R^{\mathrm{I}}/\partial\pi_c^*$ increases. For even higher efficiencies, the η_c^* term of the differential equation (1.51) $\left(\frac{\partial L_R^{\mathrm{I}}}{\partial\pi_c^*}+l\frac{\partial L_R^{\mathrm{II}}}{\partial T_g^*}\right)$ will amount altogether to

1·5–2 per cent of the first term, corresponding to the ideal cycle. The signs of these terms are opposite.

In the case of high efficiencies, the remaining terms of the equation will also similarly amount to a small percentage of the first term.

Thus for example, the losses in a combustion chamber from incomplete liberation of heat is expressed by the equation

$$L_R^{II} = q\frac{H_u}{A}\eta_t(1-\eta_z);$$

$$\frac{\partial L_R^{II}}{\partial T_g^*} = 0; \quad \frac{\partial L_R^{II}}{\partial \pi_c^*} = q\frac{H_u}{A}(1-\eta_z)\frac{k_g-1}{k_g}\frac{1}{\pi_c^{*(2k_g-1)/k_g}}$$

$$\text{When } \pi_c^* \to \infty, \text{ then } \frac{\partial L_R^{II}}{\partial \pi_c^*} \to 0.$$

The ratio of the term in equation (1.51), taking into account the losses L_R^{II}, to the first term is approximately $(1-\eta_z)$. Consequently, for high values of $\eta_z = 0{\cdot}97 - 0{\cdot}98$ this ratio will amount in all to 2–3 per cent.

For a small relative value of the terms in equation (1.51) containing derivatives of the loss in the engine units, extremely high values of π_c^* and T_g^* are required in order that equation (1.51) should be equal to zero. An increase in π_c^* and T_g^* will also be promoted by the circumstance for which certain terms, containing derivatives of the losses, will have the same sign as the derivatives of the losses in an ideal cycle. For example, the derivatives with respect to π_{c0}^* of the aerodynamic losses in the combustion chamber and the derivatives with respect to T_g^* of the losses in the turbine have the minus sign, i.e. the same sign as the derivatives with respect to π_c^* of L_{Ri}. Therefore, for sufficiently high efficiencies it can be assumed that the solution to equation (1.51) will, in practice, fit the conditions $\pi_c^* \to \infty$ and $T_g^* \to \infty$.

If the efficiency of the units is reduced, then since the terms of equation (1.51) containing derivatives of the losses increase, this equation as a consequence can also be transformed into zero for certain finite values of π_c^* and T_g^*. This will indicate that for the values indicated of π_c^* and T_g^*, there is at once a minimum C_R with respect to the two variables. Since for an increase in efficiency the losses AL_R in the cycle increase, then, as it follows from what has been said above, the attainment of a minimum also becomes possible only for high values of qH_u, i.e. at high temperatures of the gas and at high expansion ratios. Figure 5 shows the relationship $C_R = f\,(T_g^*)$ for different values of π_c^* for high and

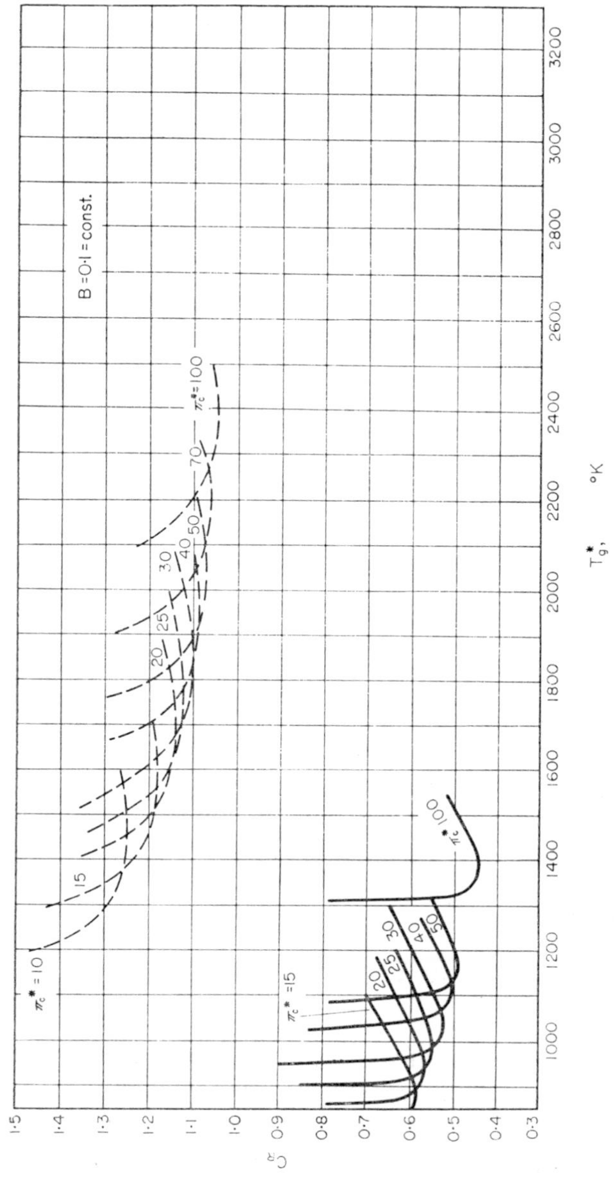

Fig. 5. Dependence of $C_R = f\,(T_g^*)$ for different values of π_c^* for high and low values ofe fficiency.

——— $\eta_c^* = 0{\cdot}8$; $\eta_t^* = 0{\cdot}92$; $\sigma_\Sigma = 0{\cdot}92$.

— — — $\eta_c^* = 0{\cdot}7$; $\eta_t^* = 0{\cdot}75$; $\sigma_\Sigma = 0{\cdot}8$.

low values of the efficiency of the compressor and of the turbine. For high efficiencies the minimum values of C_R, obtained for $\pi_c^* =$ $=$const., are monotonically reduced according to the extent of in crease of π_c^* and T_g^*.

For lower efficiencies the minimum values of C_R are first of all likewise monotonically reduced, but then this reduction ceases, which characterizes the appearance of the minimum with respect to the two variables. However, this occurs in the region of unrealistically high values of T_g^* and π_c^*. Consequently, the theoretical possibility of the existence of a minimum with respect to the two variables for reduced efficiencies has no practical significance. What has been said above corresponds to the condition $B=$const., which is equivalent to constant specific heat in the combustion chamber.

If the variation of the coefficient B is taken into consideration, then the latter increases with increase of temperature; in principle this is equivalent to a deterioration inefficiency, since it is associated with an increase in the fuel consumption.

Therefore the appearance of a minimum with respect to two variables can be expected for certain values of T_g^* and π_c^*.

Figure 6 shows the dependence of $C_R=f\,(T_g^*)$ for variable values of B for high and low values of efficiency; for high efficiencies the minimum C_R with respect to the two variables does not occur even at unrealistic values of π_c^* ($\pi_c^* \geq 100$). For reduced efficiencies a minimum with respect to the two variables is obtained, but for extremely high values of π_c^* (~ 50) and of the gas temperature ($T_g^* \approx 2000$°K). It should be noted that for high values of T_g^* and π_c^*, the variable specific heat in the processes of compression and expansion begins to exert a considerable effect on C_R. These problems will be discussed briefly below.

According to the equation stated

$$\frac{\partial C_R}{\partial \pi_c^*}=0 \text{ and } \frac{\partial C_R}{\partial T_g^*}=0$$

it is necessary to consider them separately and to find the minimum values of C_R at constant gas temperature or at constant expansion ratio, since the conditions for which simultaneous solutions to these equations are achieved are of no practical importance.

It should be noted that minimum C_R with respect to gas temperature or π_c^* will not correspond to minimum C_R with respect to q and L_R for $\pi_c^* = \text{const.}$ or for $T_g^* = \text{const.}$

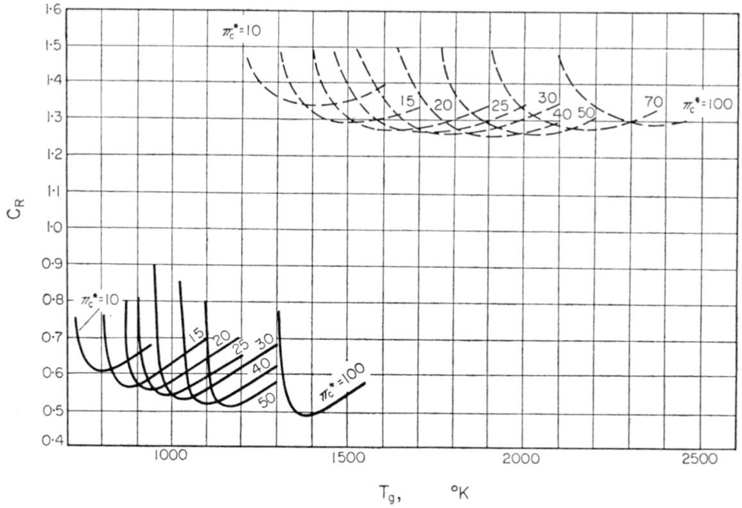

Fig. 6. Dependence of $C_R = f(T_g^*)$ for different values of π_c^* and variable B.

$$\eta_c^* = 0{\cdot}85;\ \eta_t^* = 0{\cdot}92;\ \sigma_\Sigma = 0{\cdot}92.$$
$$\eta_c^* = 0{\cdot}7;\ \eta_t^* = 0{\cdot}75;\ \sigma_\Sigma = 0{\cdot}85.$$

Actually, since $C_R = f(\pi_c^*; T_g^*)$ and $\pi_c^* = f(q; T_g^*)$, then for $T_g^* = \text{const.}$ we can write

$$\frac{dC_R}{dq} = \frac{dC_R}{d\pi_c^*}\,\frac{d\pi_c^*}{dq}\,.$$

Analogous with this, for $\pi_c^* = \text{const.}$,

$$\frac{dC_R}{dq} = \frac{dC_R}{dT_g^*}\,\frac{dT_g^*}{dq}\,.$$

If $\dfrac{dC_R}{d\pi_c^*} = 0$ or $\dfrac{dC_R}{dT_g^*} = 0$, then also $\dfrac{dC_R}{dq} = 0$. By contrast to the previous instance, we shall write the total derivative with respect to q for C_R, which in the given case corresponds to $T_g^* = \text{const.}$ or to $\pi_c^* = \text{const.}$

Similarly, we can obtain the relationship

$$\frac{dC_R}{dL_R} \text{ from } \frac{dC_R}{d\pi_c^*} \text{ and from } \frac{dC_R}{dT_g^*}.$$

Figure 7 shows the dependence of C_R and AL_R on qH_u.

It can be seen from curves 2 and 3 that the minimum C_R is obtained for considerably lower values of qH_u than for AL_R=const. (curve 1).

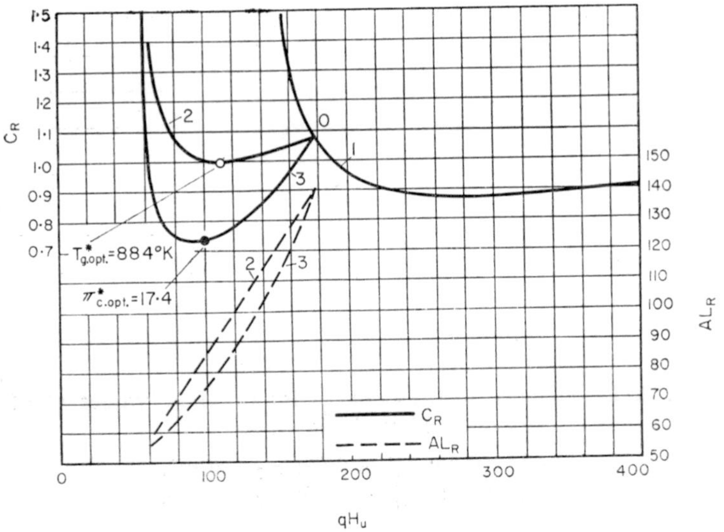

Fig. 7. Dependence of C_R and AL_R on qH_u for $H = 0$, $M = 0$. (1) AL_R = const. = 140·3 cal/kg; (2) π_c^* = const. = 4·5; (3) T_g^* = const. = 1100° K.

For the point 0 and curves 2 and 3; $\eta_c^* = 0{\cdot}778$; $\eta_t^* = 0{\cdot}876$; $a = 0{\cdot}876$; $B = 0{\cdot}0985$; $\nu\varphi_V = 1{\cdot}015$; H_u = 10,500 cal/kg.

It is important to note that the law of variation of losses in the cycle of a turbo-jet engine depends upon the fact that π_c^* or T_g^* are maintained constant.

In particular, for T_g^*=const. and for an increasing π_c^*, the losses initially will be reduced more intensively than in the case of π_c^*= =const. and T_g^*=var. (see Fig. 7), since the temperature of the gases discharging from the engine is strongly reduced in the first case.

The different laws of variation of losses in the cycle as a function of π_c^* and T_g^* are virtually the physical reason for the absence of a minimum C_R with respect to the two variables within the limits of actual possible values of π_c^*, T_g^*, and efficiencies.

It should be noted that the optimum expansion ratio for $T_g^* = \text{const.}$ is always found at the same part of the curve $C_R = f\,(T_g^*)$, where C_R increases with reduction of gas temperature, and which can be easily seen, for example, from the curves given in Figs. 5 and 6 if the variation of π_c^* for $T_g^* = \text{const.}$ be considered. Consequently, the optimum expansion ratio at regimes associated with reduction of the gas temperature will be disadvantageous.

Moreover, in considering the optimum value of π_c^* on the curve $C_R = f\,(T_g^*)$ it can be seen that it is sufficient for the same π_c^* to increase the temperature of the gas relatively little, in order to obtain a regime with a lower specific fuel consumption, to which will correspond the optimum gas temperature.

Therefore the study of $C_{R\min}$, attained for optimum gas temperature with $\pi_c^* = \text{const.}$ presents the most interest.

It should also be taken into consideration that in a turbo-jet engine a gas is used at a sufficiently high temperature, which is optimum for high expansion ratios (see p. 47.). An exception are high supersonic velocities ($M_H \geq 2{\cdot}5 - 3{\cdot}0$), for which the gas temperature ($T_g^* \approx 1150°\text{K}$) of modern turbo-jet engines becomes optimum for small expansion ratios (see p. 50.).

However, if it be taken into consideration that with an increase in the temperature of the gas, the values of π_c^* are also markedly increased at which the temperature becomes optimum, and the use of a low gas temperature for large values of M_H is not characteristic, then it can be assumed that for turbo-jet engines the maximum expansion ratio is that at which a given gas temperature is optimum.

Until recently, the problems mentioned have not been paid sufficient attention in the literature, and both optimum regimes are frequently considered as equally probable, which in principle it is impossible to recognize with certainty.

Actually, for choosing the expansion ratio, one is obliged to take into consideration still further factors, for example, the dimensions and weight, which will be discussed in the next section.

For solving the equations $\dfrac{\partial C_R}{\partial \pi_c^*} = 0$ and $\dfrac{\partial C_R}{\partial T_g^*} = 0$, the remaining quantities (i.e. efficiency, etc.), as mentioned above, should have a certain finite value. Obviously, to every combination of these quantities there will correspond its value for $C_{R\min}$, as a result of which there can be an infinitely large number of minimum fuel consumptions. However, as a result of analysis the values of η_c^*, η_g^* and other quantities are limited to certain most practical values and a partial solution is obtained. As a result of change of value of even one of the coefficients, $C_{R\min}$ should be determined again.

In studying an actual engine, as a rule, the efficiency, the pressure coefficient and other quantities cannot be assumed to be independent variables, since in principle any change of operating regime of the engine also leads to a change of operating regime of all its units.

However, the problem of attaining minimum specific fuel consumption can be considered only in the case when the required thrust is less than the maximum for a given flight velocity, since only in this case is there the possibility of varying the gas temperature and the expansion ratio.

Derivation and Analysis of Equations for Determining the Optimum Gas Temperature and the Optimum Expansion Ratio

The solution of the equations $\partial C_R/\partial T_g^*=0$ and $\partial R_R/\partial \pi_c^*=0$ for determining the optimum temperature of the gas and the optimum expansion ratio is associated with well-known difficulties, as a consequence of which there has been no general solution of these equations until recently.

Only the solution of the equation $\partial C_R/\partial T_g^*=0$ is known, obtained by Prof. I. I. Kulagin[1] under certain assumptions. We shall consider this solution below.

If equation (1.30) be used for determining C_R, then the task of finding the optimum temperature of the gas and $\pi_{c\ \text{opt}}^*$ is somewhat facilitated as a consequence of the fact that the same variables (T_g^*, π_c^*, η_c^* etc) enter indirectly into this equation, also their functions $\Phi\ (q)$; $R\ (\pi_n)$, etc. However, for this it is necessary to make a number of simplifying assumptions and, in particular, to assume constant the coefficients B and a, although they depend

[1] I. I. Kulagin, *Theory of Aircraft Gas-Turbine Engines*, Oborongiz, 1955.

upon the gas temperature and the expansion ratio, but this dependence is complex and cannot be expressed analytically.

As shown below, the assumption concerning the constancy of the quantity B and of the specific heat on the compression and expansion curves, upon which, in particular, a depends, bears certain quantitative differences but not differences in principle in relation to accurate calculations.

Taking equation (1.30) initially, it is convenient to consider as the minimum not C_R but $C_{Rp}=C_R' B\sqrt{(T^*_H)}$ and as an independent variable to take not T^*_g but the ratio T^*_g/T^*_H, which permits the solution to be used for all flight altitudes.

We shall derive the partial differential of C_{Rp} with respect to any of the independent variables and we shall equate it to zero. Then the partial derivatives of $\Phi\ (q)$; $R\ (\pi_n)$ enter into the equation, which for abbreviation of writing we shall denote by a prime,[1]

$$\left[\nu\varphi_V\sqrt{\left(\frac{T^*_t}{T^*_H}\right)}R(\pi_n)-1{\cdot}87\lambda_H\right]\Phi'(q)-$$

$$-\Phi(q)\left[\nu\varphi_V\sqrt{\left(\frac{T^*_t}{T^*_H}\right)}R(\pi_n)-1{\cdot}87\lambda_H\right]'=0.$$

Opening the brackets we obtain

$$\nu\varphi_V\sqrt{\left(\frac{T^*_t}{T^*_H}\right)}R(\pi_n)\Phi'(q)-1{\cdot}87\lambda_H\Phi'(q)-\nu\varphi_c\Phi(q)\sqrt{\left(\frac{T^*_t}{T^*_H}\right)}R'(\pi^*_n)-$$

$$-\nu\varphi_V\Phi(q)R(\pi_n)\left[\sqrt{\left(\frac{T^*_t}{T^*_H}\right)}\right]'=0.$$

Dividing the equation by

$$\nu\varphi_V\sqrt{\left(\frac{T^*_t}{T^*_H}\right)}R(\pi_n)\Phi(q),$$

we obtain

$$\frac{R'(\pi_n)}{R(\pi_n)}=\frac{\Phi'(q)}{\Phi(q)}-\frac{\left[\sqrt{\left(\frac{T^*_t}{T^*_H}\right)}\right]'}{\sqrt{\left(\frac{T^*_t}{T^*_H}\right)}}-\frac{1{\cdot}87\lambda_H\Phi'(q)}{\nu\varphi_V\sqrt{\left(\frac{T^*_t}{T^*_H}\right)}R(\pi_n)\Phi(q)} \qquad (1.52)$$

[1] Assuming that $\delta_{cool}=$ const.

In this form, equation (1.52) is suitable for determining the optimum gas temperature (or T_g^*/T_H^*) and also the optimum expansion ratio, depending upon with respect to which of these parameters the partial derivatives is taken. This equation is also suitable for the case with total expansion and for a convergent nozzle with incomplete expansion, dependent upon which expression will be assumed for $R(\pi_n)$.

When the derivatives are taken with respect to T_g^*/T_H^*, for the case with total expansion we obtain

$$\frac{\Phi'(q)}{\Phi(q)} = \frac{1}{\Phi(q)}; \quad \frac{R'(\pi_n)}{R(\pi_n)} = \frac{(\pi_n^{(k_g-1)/k_g})'}{2(\pi_n^{2(k_g-1)/k_g} - \pi_n^{(k_g-1)/k_g}} =$$

$$= \frac{(\delta_\Sigma \pi_c^* \pi_V)^{(k_g-1)/k_g} \dfrac{al(\pi_c^*)}{\eta_t^*(T^*/T_H^*)^2}}{2(\pi_n^{2(k_g-1)/k_g} - \pi_n^{(k_g-1)/k_g})}; \quad \frac{\left(\sqrt{\left\{\dfrac{T_t^*}{T_H^*}\right\}}\right)'}{\sqrt{\left(\dfrac{T_t^*}{T_H^*}\right)}} = \frac{1}{2\dfrac{T_t^*}{T_H^*}}.$$

Denoting

$$(\delta_\Sigma \pi_c^* \pi_V)^{(k_g-1)/k_g} = b; \quad \frac{1 \cdot 87 \lambda_H}{\nu \varphi_V \sqrt{\left(\dfrac{T_t^*}{T_H^*}\right)} R(\pi_n) \Phi(q)} = f;$$

$$\frac{1}{\Phi(q)} - \frac{1}{2\dfrac{T_t}{T_H}} = J.$$

we obtain the equation for $\pi_n^{(k_g-1)/k_g} = x$ in the form

$$x^2 - x - b \frac{al(\pi_c^*)}{2\eta_t^* \left(\dfrac{T_g^*}{T_H^*}\right)^2 (J-f)} = 0\,.$$

Whence

$$x = \pi_{n.\text{opt}}^{(k_g-1)/k_g} = \frac{1 + \sqrt{\left(1 + 2b \dfrac{al(\pi_c^*)}{\eta_t^*(T_g^*/T_H^*)^2 (J-f)}\right)}}{2}. \quad (1.53)$$

Equation (1.53) can be solved graphically. For the values assumed for η_c^*, η_t^*, λ_H, $l(\pi_c^*)$ it is necessary to assign certain values to T_g^*/T_H^* and to calculate J, π_n, $R(\pi_n)$ and f. After this π_n is calculated according to formula (1.41). Plotting graphically both values of π_n as a function of T_g^*/T_H^*, we obtain at the intersection $\pi_{n\,\mathrm{opt}}$ and $(T_g^*/T_H^*)_{\mathrm{opt}}$.

The solution is considerably simplified if tables or graphs are available for the functions $\Phi\,(q)$, T_g^*/T_H^*, J and $R\,(\pi_n)$.

Another method of solving equation (1.53) is more convenient. The expansion ratio in the jet pipe can be written in the form

$$\pi_c^{(k_g-1)/k_g} = b\,\frac{T_{t.\mathrm{ad}}}{T_g}\,.$$

where $T_{t.\mathrm{ad}}$ is the temperature of the gas after the turbine for adiabatic expansion

$$\frac{T_{t.\mathrm{ad}}^*}{T_H^*} = \frac{T_g^*}{T_H^*} - a\,\frac{l(\pi_c^*)}{\eta_t^*}\,.$$

Substituting in equation (1.53) the expression for π_n deduced above and solving it with respect to b, we obtain

$$b = \frac{T_g^*/T_H^*}{T_{t.\mathrm{ad}}^*/T_H^*}\left[1 + \frac{a l(\pi_c^*)\,\dfrac{T_H^*}{T_g^*}}{2\eta_t^*\,\dfrac{T_{t.\mathrm{ad}}^*}{T_H^*}\,(J-f)}\right]. \tag{1.54}$$

This equation can also be solved graphically in relation to the coefficient b, which also enters into the right-hand portion of the equation [into the coefficient f via $R\,(\pi_n)$].

Equation (1.54) simplifies the calculation in relation to equation (1.53) as a consequence of the fact that with a change of b the coefficient J remains unaltered and it is only necessary to determine the new value of $R\,(\pi_n)$ and of f.

Moreover, when the flight velocity $V=0$ and, consequently, $f=0$, then this equation enables the coefficient b to be calculated directly.

It should be noted that when $l\,(\pi_c^*)=0$, i.e. $\pi_c^*=1{\cdot}0$, then $(J-f)$ is also equal to zero and $b=(\delta_\Sigma\,\pi_V)^{(k_g-1)/k_g}$

For $l\,(\pi_c^*)=0$ $(T_g^*/T_H^*)_{\mathrm{opt}}$ $J-f=0$ is determined from the equation.

For all other values of (π_c^*), the coefficient b should be satisfied by the condition $J>f$.

If it be assumed that for $\Phi\,(q)=0$ $R_{\mathrm{sp}}=0$, then the limiting value of the specific fuel consumption will be expressed by the ratio 0/0.

For this the coefficient b should have a finite value complying with the equation

$$b_{\lim} = \frac{1}{\dfrac{T_H^*}{T_g^*}\,\dfrac{T_{t.\mathrm{ad}}^*}{T_H^*}\left[1-\left(\dfrac{0{\cdot}382\lambda_H}{\nu\varphi_V\sqrt{(T_t^*/T_H^*)}}\right)^2\right]}\,.$$

For this, it is necessary to bear in mind that the value $C_R = 0/0$ for an actual cycle is impracticable and at the most it is taken only in the nature of a provisory limit, by the proximity to which the individual coefficients (η_c^*, η_t^*, δ_Σ, etc.) can have values greater than 1·0.

The equations obtained, (1.53) and (1.54), show that without the use of functions of the form $\Phi(q)$, $R(\pi_n)$ and T_t^*/T_H^*, depending on the primary variables T_g^* and π_c^*, it is impossible, without additional simplifications, to solve the problem concerning the optimum temperature of the gas, since this temperature cannot be expressed in an explicit form. As will be shown below, a similar solution is also obtained for the optimum expansion ratio. The problem concerning the optimum temperature of the gas can be solved in an explicit form by making additional assumptions.

Figures 8 and 9 depict the plot of optimum values for T_H^*/T_g^* for constant turbine efficiency and constant product $\nu\varphi_V$, calculated by means of equation (1.54). As parameters, $l(\pi_c^*)$, and $b = (\delta_\Sigma \pi_c^* \pi_V)^{(k_g-1)/k_g}$ have been taken, which gives a sufficiently generalized character to the result obtained, in so far as they show the influence on $(T_H^*/T_g^*)_{\mathrm{opt}}$ of the different values of π_c^*, η_c^* and δ_Σ.

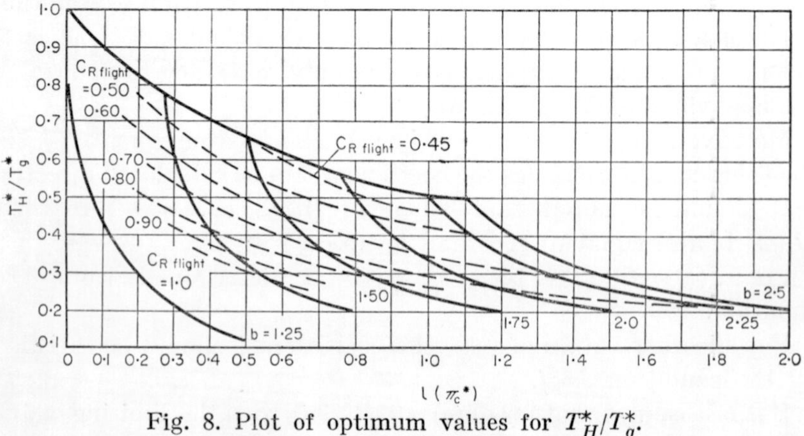

Fig. 8. Plot of optimum values for T_H^*/T_g^*.
$\lambda_H = M_H = 1{\cdot}0$; $\eta_t^* = 0{\cdot}9$; $\nu\varphi_V = 0{\cdot}975$.

Curves of constant values of $C_{R\text{flight}}$ are plotted on this same graph, which are found to be minimum at each point. The curves in Fig. 8 and 9 show graphically the non-equivalence, pointed out earlier, of the concept concerning the optimum value of T_g^*/T_H^*, since, dependent upon the efficiency and δ_Σ, it is possible to have different optimum values of T_g^*/T_H^*, with respect to magnitude, for $\pi_c^* = \text{const.}$ and one and the same value of $(T_g^*/T_H^*)_{\text{opt}}$ and $C_{R\min}$ for different expansion ratios.

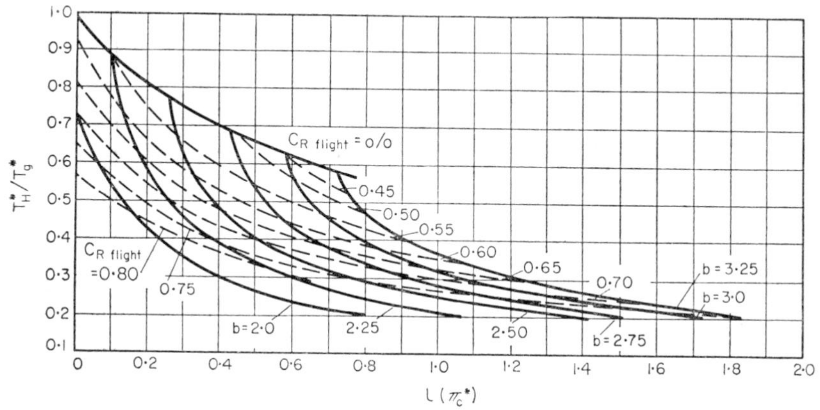

Fig. 9. Plot of optimum values of T_H^*/T_g^* for $M_H = 2{\cdot}5$, $\eta_t^* = 0{\cdot}9$; $\nu\varphi_V = 0{\cdot}975$.

If it be assumed that on the line $b = \text{const.}$ the expansion ratio and consequently also δ_Σ, remain constant[1], then this line will show the effect on $(T_H^*/T_g^*)_{\text{opt}}$ or on $(T_g^*/T_H^*)_{\text{opt}}$ of the compressor efficiency, which should increase with increase in T_H^*/T_g^* and which can be determined according to the equation

$$\eta_c^* = \frac{\pi_c^{*(k-1)/k} - 1}{l(\pi_c^*)}.$$

Thus for example, if in Fig. 8 we take $\delta_\Sigma \pi_c^* = 8{\cdot}47$, $b = 2{\cdot}0$ and $\pi_c^* = 9{\cdot}5$ $(\delta_\Sigma = 0{\cdot}89)$, then for $l\,(\pi_c^*) = 1{\cdot}5$, $\eta_c^* = 0{\cdot}602$ and for $l(\pi_c^*) = 1{\cdot}0$, $\eta_c^* = 0{\cdot}904$.

For $l\,(\pi_*^c) = 1{\cdot}5$ and $l\,(\pi_c^*) = 1{\cdot}0$, the values of $(T_H^*/T_g^*)_{\text{opt}}$ are correspondingly equal to 0·2 and 0·33.

[1] For $M_H = \text{const.}$ $\pi_V = \text{const.}$ it is also assumed that $(k_g - 1)/k_g = \text{const} = 0{\cdot}25$.

Further reduction of $l\,(\pi_c^*)$ for the same initial data can lead to $\eta^* < 1{\cdot}0$, since the value of $C_{R\min}$ approaches the value 0/0, which in an actual cycle cannot be obtained.

If it be assumed that $\eta_c^* = \text{const.}$ then the line $b = \text{const.}$ or $\delta_\Sigma \pi_c^* = \text{const.}$ will exert an influence on δ_Σ, which should vary along this line according to the equation

$$\delta_\Sigma = \frac{(\delta_\Sigma \pi_c^*)}{[1 - \eta_c^* l(\pi_c)^*]^{k/(k-1)}}\,.$$

For $\delta_\Sigma \pi_c^* = 8{\cdot}47$ $(b = 2{\cdot}0)$ with $\eta_c^* = 0{\cdot}85$ we obtain: if $l\,(\pi_c^*) = 1{\cdot}5$, then $\delta_\Sigma = 0{\cdot}48$ and $\pi_c^* = 17{\cdot}6$, and, when $l\,(\pi_c^*) = 1{\cdot}0$, then $\delta_\Sigma = 0{\cdot}985$ and $\pi_c^* = 8{\cdot}6$. The corresponding values of $(T_H^*/T_g^*)_{\text{opt}}$ are equal, and as previously to 0·2 and 0·33.

The examples presented show that it is only possible to obtain a low optimum gas temperature (or a high value of T_H^*/T_g^* for small losses in the cycle. With increased losses (in the compressor or in other units) the optimum gas temperature increases, which was pointed out above.

If it be assumed that $\pi_c^* = \text{const.}$ and $\eta_c^* = \text{const.}$ then the effect of δ_Σ on $(T_H^*/T_g^*)_{\text{opt}}$ will be characterized by the vertical sections and the value of δ_Σ may be determined from the ratio

$$\frac{\delta_\Sigma}{\delta_{\Sigma 0}} = \frac{(T_H^*/T_g^*)_0}{T_H^*/T_g^*}\,,$$

where the quantity with the index "0" corresponds to the regime adopted initially.

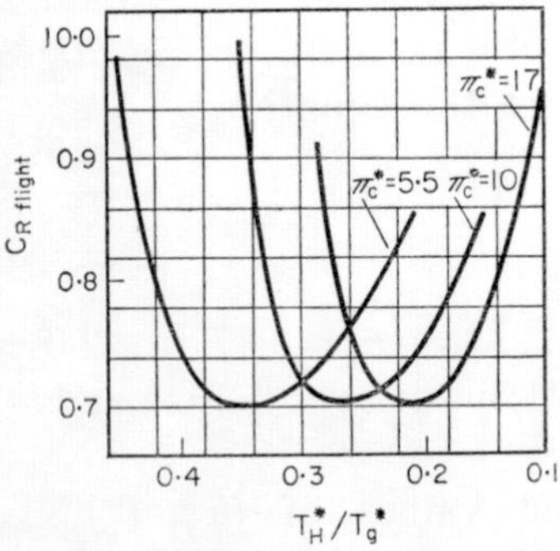

Fig. 10*a*.
Variation of $C_{R\,\text{flight}}$ for $C_{R\min} = \text{const.}$ and $M_H = 1{\cdot}0$.

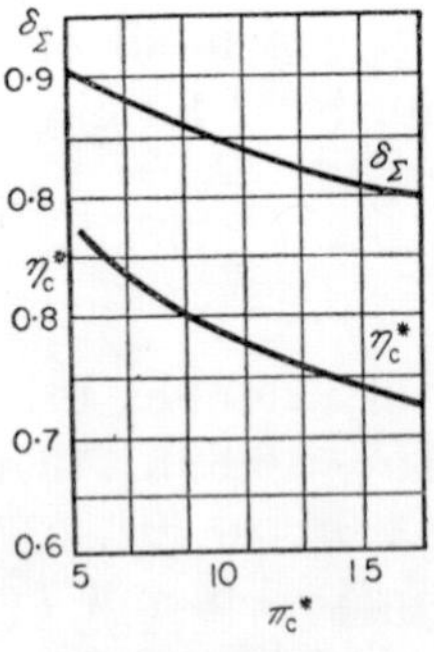

Fig. 10*b*.
Variation of δ_Σ and η_c^* for $C_{R\min} = \text{const.}$ and $M_H = 1{\cdot}0$

With a reduction in the efficiency of the compressor or in δ_Σ according to the extent of the increase of π_c^*, $C_{R\,\min}$ may remain constant and the relationship $C_{R\,\text{flight}} = f\,(T_g^*/T_H^*)$ acquires the form shown in Fig. 10a. In this graph, the corresponding values of $\delta_c^* = f\,(\pi_c^*)$ are shown for $\eta_c^* =$ const. and the values $\eta_c^* = f\,(\pi_c^*)$ for $\delta_\Sigma =$ const. Finally, in the case of increase of efficiency and of δ_Σ according to the extent of the increase of π_c^* it is possible to obtain $(T_H^*/T_g^*)_{\text{opt}} =$ const. for all values of π_c^* (Fig. 11).

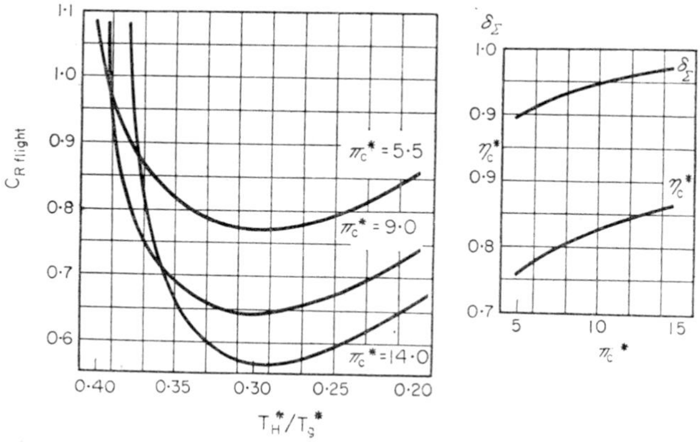

Fig. 11*a*. Variation of $C_{R\,\text{flight}}$ for $(T_H^*/T_g^*)_{\text{opt}} =$ const. and $M_H = 1$.
b. Variation of δ_Σ and η_c^* for $(T_H^**/T_g^*)_{\text{opt}} =$ const. for $M_H = 1{\cdot}0$.

For a given compressor efficiency and δ_Σ any temperature of the gas can, in the long run, be optimum in the case of choice of the corresponding expansion ratio. The latter may be found with the aid of the curves presented in Figs. 8 and 9 by means of a graphical solution of the equation

$$l(\pi_c^*) = \frac{(b/\delta_\Sigma \pi_V)^{0{\cdot}286} - 1}{\eta_c^*}\;. \tag{1.55}$$

Having assigned a number of values for b and knowing δ_Σ, π_V and η_c^* we find $l\,(\pi_c^*)$ according to equation (1.55) and then we determine $(T_H^*/T_g^*)_{\text{opt}}$ according to the curves shown in Figs. 8 and 9.

The value of $l\,(\pi_H^*)$, for which the given ratio of T_H^*/T_g^* will be obtained, will be found.

Thus for example, if $T_H^*/T_g^*=0{\cdot}3$ be given ($T_g^*=867$°K for $T_H^*=260$°K), $\eta_c^*=0{\cdot}83$ and $\delta_\Sigma=0{\cdot}92$, then for $\lambda_H=1{\cdot}0$ the unknown expansion ratio, for which a given T_H^*/T_g^* is optimum, will be equal to $\pi_c^*=9{\cdot}2$.

If $T_H^*/T_g^*=0{\cdot}25$ ($T_g^*=1040$°K for $T_H^*=260$°K), then $\pi_c^*=20$.

This example shows that even for a relatively low gas temperature a high expansion ratio is required, because of the fact that this temperature was optimum. For comparison, let us determine the optimum expansion ratio for the same value of the gas temperature.

The equation for determining the optimum expansion ratio can be obtained from the original equation (1.52). For simplification it is convenient to take the partial derivatives not with respect to the expansion ratio but with respect to $l\,(\pi_c^*)$.

Hence we obtain

$$\frac{\Phi'(q)}{\Phi(q)}=-\frac{1}{\Phi(q)};\quad \frac{(\sqrt{[T_t^*/T_H^*]})'}{\sqrt{(T_t^*/T_H^*)}}=-\frac{a}{2T_t^*/T_H^*};$$
$$\frac{R'(\pi_n)}{R(\pi_n)}=\frac{(\pi_n{}^{(k_g-1)/k_g})'}{2(\pi_n{}^{(2k_g-1)/k_g}-\pi_n{}^{(k_g-1)/k_g})}.$$

The partial derivative of $\pi_n^{(k_g-1)/k_g}$ with respect to $l\,(\pi_c^*)$ has the form

$$\frac{\partial\pi_c{}^{(k_g-1)/k_g}}{\partial l(\pi_c^*)}=-b\frac{a}{\eta_t^*\dfrac{T_g^*}{T_H^*}}+\pi_c{}^{(k_g-1)/k_g}\frac{k_g-1}{k_g}\,\frac{k}{k-1}\,\frac{\eta_c^*}{\pi_c^{*(k-1)/k}}.$$

Denoting

$$J_\pi=\frac{a}{2\dfrac{T_t^*}{T_H^*}}-\frac{1}{\Phi(q)}$$

and using the values obtained for the derivatives, we obtain the following equation for the coefficient $b=(\delta_\Sigma\pi_c^*\pi_V)^{k_g-1/k_g}$

$$b=\frac{\dfrac{T_g^*}{T_H^*}}{\dfrac{T_{t.\mathrm{ad}}^*}{T_H^*}}\left[1+\frac{\dfrac{T_{t.\mathrm{ad}}^*}{T_H^*}\,\dfrac{k_g-1}{k_g}\,\dfrac{k}{k-1}\,\dfrac{\eta_k}{\pi_c^{*(k-1)/k}}\,\dfrac{a}{\eta_t^*}}{2\dfrac{T_{t.\mathrm{ad}}^*}{T_H^*}(J_\pi+f)}\right] \tag{1.56}$$

where the same function, as before, (see page 42.) is denoted by f.

Equation (1.56) should also be solved graphically.

Figures 12 and 13 show the plots of optimum values of $\pi_c^* = f = (T_H^*/T_g^*)$ obtained according to equation (1.56) for several values, of η_c^* and δ_Σ. The efficiency of the turbine and the product $\nu\varphi_V$ just as previously, are taken to be constant. From Fig. 12 we find the value of $\pi_{c\,opt}^*$ for $T_H^*/T_g^* = 0{\cdot}3$ and for $T_H^*/T_g^* = 0{\cdot}25$ correspondingly 17·0 and $\approx 34{\cdot}0$.

Thus, the optimum expansion ratio is substantially higher than the values of π_c^* obtained previously. However, the gain in specific fuel consumption for an increase in π_c^* from 20 to 34 amounts to not more than 4 – 5 per cent, even for conservation of efficiency, which is difficult to attain.

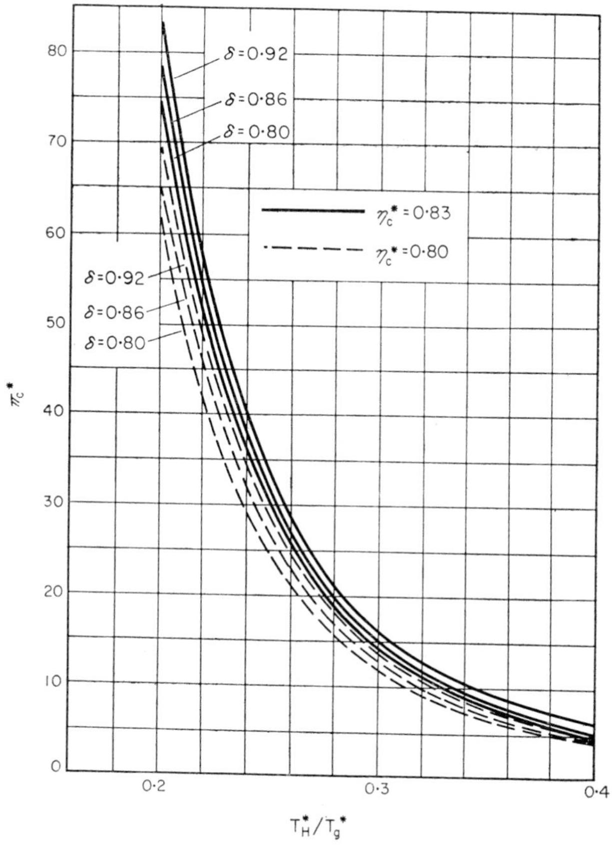

Fig. 12. Plot of optimum values of π_c^* for $\lambda_H = M_H = 1{\cdot}0$, $\eta_t^* = 0{\cdot}9$ and $\nu\varphi_v = 0{\cdot}975$.

Moreover, such an increase in the expansion ratio gives rise to an increase in the weight and the dimensions of the engine.

This example confirms the opinion expressed previously concerning the fact that the maximum expansion ratio which can be used to advantage, is that for which a given maximum gas temperature is optimum.

Finally, if it be assumed that it will be possible to achieve $\pi_c^* = 34$ with adequate efficiency and acceptable weight characteristics, then it is sufficient to increase the temperature of the gas from 1040° K to 1150° K in order to obtain for this π_c^* the optimum gas temperature and additionally to reduce the specific fuel consumption by ~2 per cent.

Thus, the optimum temperature of the gas with respect to efficiency should be regarded as a primary parameter, which, amongst others, should also be taken into consideration for choosing the expansion ratio.

For an increase in the flight velocity, there occurs a considerable increase in the optimum gas temperature even for identical values of π_c^*; η_c^*; δ_Σ, as indicated in Fig. 14, where the field of optimum values of T_g^* is plotted for two velocities $M_H = 1{\cdot}0$ and $M_H = 2{\cdot}5$. For convenience of comparison, the absolute gas temperature is plotted along the ordinate axis on the assumption that the flight altitude is identical and equal to 11 km.

At the same time it should be noted that for a flight velocity of $M_H = 2{\cdot}5$ the pressure coefficient δ_Σ will be less and this involves an additional increase of $T_{g.\mathrm{opt}}^*$.

As a consequence of the increase of the optimum gas temperature as a result of increasing the flight velocity, the very same gas temperature will, in the case of high velocities, become optimum for lower values of the expansion ratio.

Thus, as was indicated above, for a flight velocity corresponding to $M_H = 1{\cdot}0$, the gas temperature of 1150°K will be optimum if $\pi_c^* = 34$. For $M_H = 2{\cdot}5$, this same gas temperature will be optimum for an expansion ratio of $\pi_c^* = 2{\cdot}6$,[1] if it be assumed, just as in the previous example, that $\eta_c^* = 0{\cdot}83$ and $\eta_t^* = 0{\cdot}90$ but $\delta_\Sigma = 0{\cdot}68$.

The optimum expansion ratio for T_g^* 1150°K, in the case when

[1] If this expansion ratio leads to flight conditions for $M = 1{\cdot}0$ then it will be equal to five.

$M_H = 2{\cdot}5$, is equal to $5{\cdot}5 - 6{\cdot}0$, i.e., it is relatively small. However, using $T_g^* = 1150$°K for $M_H = 2{\cdot}5$ does not appear to be characteristic, as already mentioned above, and with increase of gas temperature a strong increase in $\pi_{c\,opt}^*$ occurs (see Fig. 13).

It is necessary to take into consideration also that for optimum values of π_c^* the dimensions of the compressor and turbine should considerably increase, as shown in the foregoing section. Con-

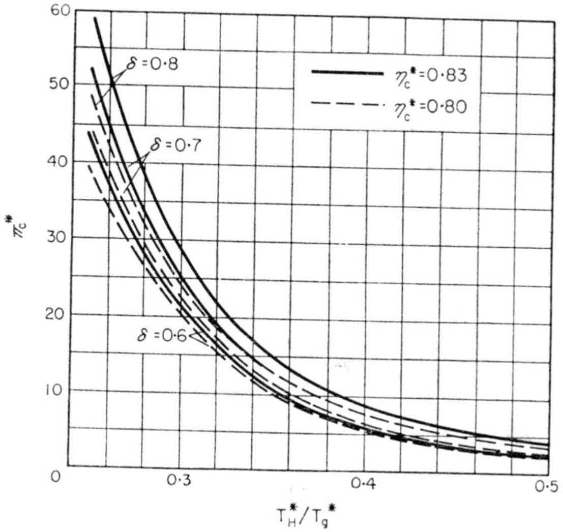

Fig. 13. Plot of optimum values of π_c^* for $M_H = 2{\cdot}5$ ($\lambda_H = 1{\cdot}285$), $\eta_t^* = 0{\cdot}90$ and $\nu\varphi_V = 0{\cdot}975$.

sequently, for these flight velocities the overall assumption can be made, that the maximum practical expansion ratio expedient for use, is, as a rule, that for which a given temperature is optimum.

In order to determine the optimum gas temperature, apart from equation (1.54), which requires a graphical solution, an approximate but sufficiently accurate equation can be obtained which will permit this gas temperature to be calculated directly.

Let us write the equation for $C_{R\,\text{flight}}$ in the form

$$C_{R\,\text{flight}} = \frac{\delta_{\text{cool}}\Phi(q)}{\nu\varphi_V \sqrt{\left(\frac{T_t^*}{T_H^*}\right)4{\cdot}9\sqrt{\left(\frac{\pi_n^{(k_g-1)/k_g}-1}{\pi_n^{(k_g-1)/k_g}}\right)}} - 1{\cdot}87\lambda_H}.$$

Since

$$\pi_n^{(k_g-1)/k_g} = b\,\frac{T_H^*}{T_g^*}\,\frac{T_{t.ad}^*}{T_H^*},$$

then the previous equation can be written as

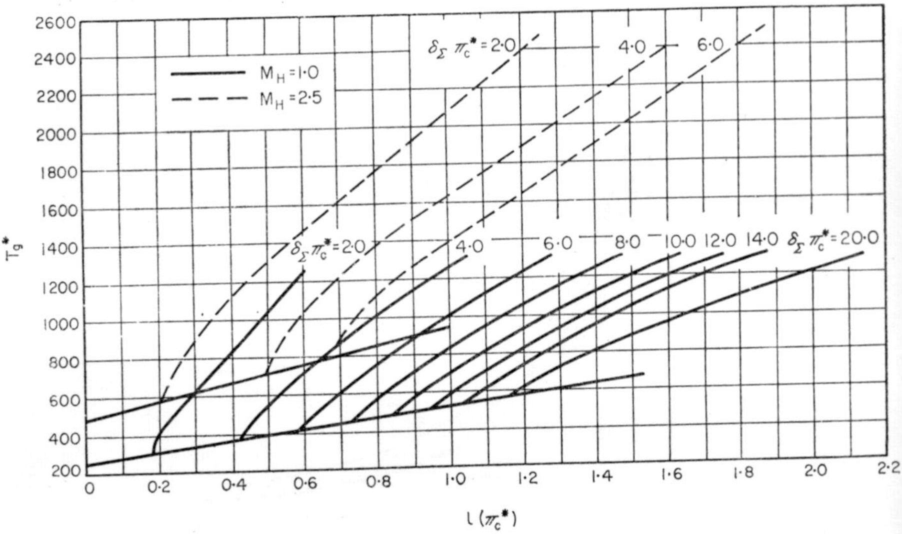

Fig. 14. Plot of maximum values of T_g^* for $M_H = 1{\cdot}0$ and $M_H = 2{\cdot}5$.

$$C_{R\text{flight}} = \frac{\delta_{\text{cool}}\Phi(q)}{4{\cdot}9\nu\varphi_V\sqrt{\left(\frac{T_g^*}{T_{t.ad}^*}\right)}\sqrt{\left[\frac{T_g^*}{T_H^*}\left(1-\frac{1}{b}\right)-a\,\frac{l(\pi_c^*)}{\eta_t^*}\right]}-1{\cdot}87\lambda_H}.$$

If we make the assumption that $T_t^* = T_{t\cdot ad}^*$ and denote the expression in the denominator under the root sign by the symbol y, then

$$C_{R\text{flight}} = \frac{\delta_{\text{cool}}\Phi(q)}{4{\cdot}9\nu\varphi_V\sqrt{y}-1{\cdot}87\lambda_H}.$$

Equating the partial derivative of $C_{R\,\text{flight}}$ with respect to T_g^*/T_H^* to zero, and, assuming that the partial derivative with respect to T_g^*/T_H^* of $\Phi(q)$ is equal to unity, and of y is equal to $1-\frac{1}{b}$, we obtain

$$2\cdot 4{\cdot}9\nu\varphi_V y - 2\cdot 1{\cdot}87\lambda_H \sqrt{(y)} - \Phi(q) 4{\cdot}9\nu\varphi_V\left(1-\frac{1}{b}\right) = 0. \quad (1.57)$$

The function $\Phi(q)$ which enters into the last term of this equation can be represented in the form of a relationship between y and $l\,(\pi_c^*)$:

$$\Phi(q) = \frac{a\dfrac{l(\pi_c^*)}{\eta_t^*}+y}{1-\dfrac{1}{b}} - [1+l(\pi_c^*)].$$

Substituting the expression obtained for $\Phi(q)$ in equation (1.57), we obtain

$$4{\cdot}9\nu\varphi_V y - 2\cdot 1{\cdot}87\lambda_H \sqrt{y} + 4{\cdot}9\nu\varphi_V\left\{[1+l(\pi_c^*)]\left(1-\frac{1}{b}\right) - a\frac{l(\pi_c^*)}{\eta_t^*}\right\} = 0.$$

Solving this equation relative to y, we find its optimum value

$$\sqrt{(y_{\text{opt}})} = \frac{1{\cdot}87\lambda_H + \sqrt{\left[(1{\cdot}87\lambda_H)^2 - (4{\cdot}9\nu\varphi_V)^2\left\{[1+l(\pi_c^*)]\left(1-\frac{1}{b}\right) - a\frac{l(\pi_c^*)}{\eta_t}\right\}\right]}}{4{\cdot}9\nu\varphi_V} \quad (1.58)$$

Calculating the value of y_{opt} for given values of λ_H, $l\,(\pi_c^*)$, b and so forth, we find the optimum ratio T_g^*/T_H^* from the following equation:

$$\left(\frac{T_g^*}{T_H^*}\right)_{\text{opt}} = \frac{a\dfrac{l(\pi_c^*)}{\eta_t^*}}{1-\dfrac{1}{b}} + \frac{y_{\text{opt}}}{1-\dfrac{1}{b}}. \quad (1.59)$$

For $\lambda_H=0$, $M_H=0$ and equation (1.59) assumes the form

$$\left(\frac{T_g^*}{T_H^*}\right)_{\text{opt}} = \frac{2al(\pi_c^*)}{\eta_t^*\left(1-\dfrac{1}{b}\right)} - [1+l(\pi_c^*)]. \quad (1.60)$$

The equations obtained enable the optimum ratio of T_g^*/T_H^* to be determined without graphical constructions. These same equations can also be used for determining π_c^*, for which a given gas temperature is optimum, if certain values of π_c^* are assigned and a graph is plotted of

$$\left(\frac{T_g^*}{T_H^*}\right)_{\text{opt}} = f(\pi_c^*) .$$

The accuracy of equations (1.59) and (1.60) is satisfactory. Figures 15 and 16 show the ratio

$$\frac{T_H^*}{T_g^*} = f[l(\pi_c^*)b] ,$$

calculated according to equations (1.54), (1.59) and (1.60). It can be seen from these figures that for $M_H = 0$ the solutions practically agree. For $M_H = 2{\cdot}5$ there are deviations and especially in the region of large values of T_H^*/T_g^* and b, which present less practical interest for these conditions. In order to increase the accuracy of equation (1.59) it is recommended that the value obtained for T_g^*/T_H^* be reduced by $2{\cdot}5 - 3{\cdot}0$ per cent. If it be assumed that in the extreme region the course of C_R is sloping, then the value of T_g^*/T_H^* obtained according to the approximate formula (1.59) will enable $C_{R_{\min}}$ to be determined with the satisfactory accuracy of ~ 1 per cent.

Equations (1.59) and (1.60) are practically identical with the equations proposed by Prof. I. I. Kulagin,[1] which is natural, since

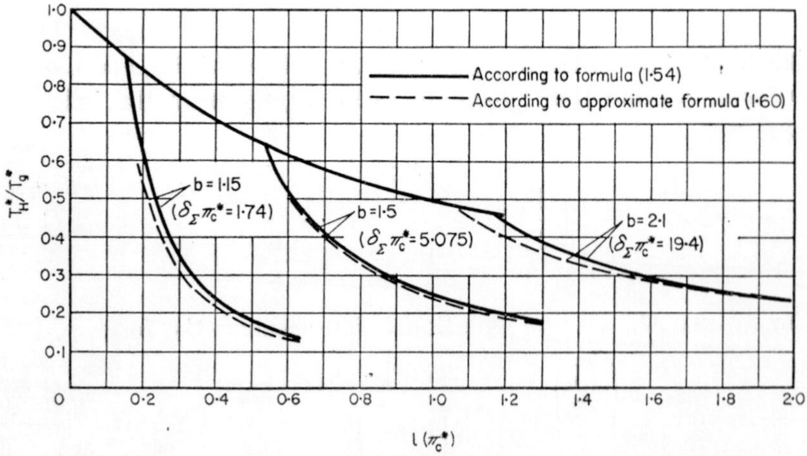

Fig. 15. Comparison between formulae (1.54) and (1.60) for determining $(T_H^*/T_g^*)_{\text{opt}}$ for $M_H = 0$.

[1] I. I. Kulagin, *Theory of Aircraft Gas Turbine Engines*, Oborongiz, 1956.

I. I. Kulagin substitutes the heat transfer h_{nozz} in the jet pipe (Fig. 17) by the heat transfer h'_{nozz} and this corresponds to the condition $T_t^* = T_{t \cdot ad}^*$.

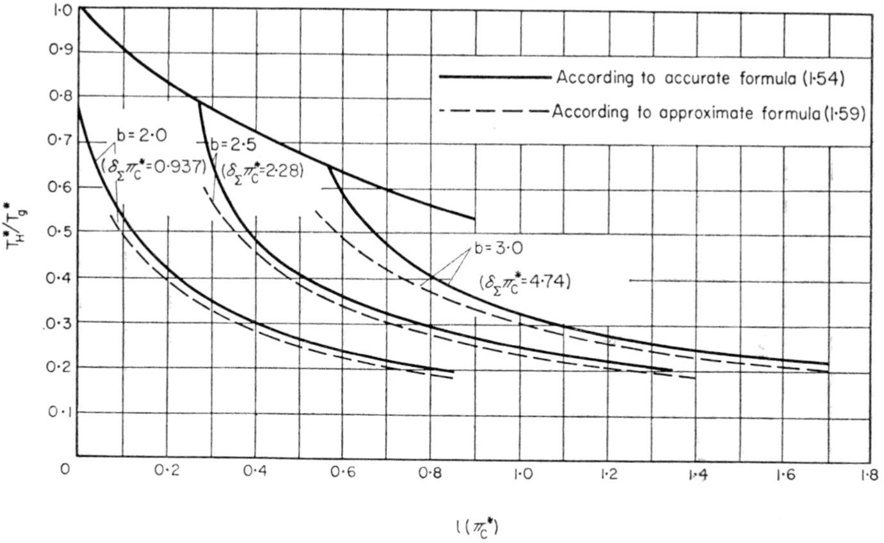

Fig. 16. Comparison between formulae (1.54) and (1.59) for determining $(T_H^*/T_g^*)_{opt}$ for $M_H = 2{\cdot}5$.

Actually, with an accuracy to that of the value of the specific heat we obtain

$$\frac{h_{nozz}}{h'_{nozz}} = \frac{T_t}{T_{t.ad}}.$$

Consequently, the condition $h_{nozz} = h'_{nozz}$ corresponds to the equation for the temperatures T_t and $T_{t.ad}$.

On the other hand,

$$T_t = T_t^* - \frac{C_t^2}{2g\dfrac{C_p}{A}} \qquad (1.61)$$

and

$$T_{t.ad} = T_{t.ad}^* - \frac{C_{t.ad}^2}{2g\dfrac{C_p}{A}}.$$

But

$$C_{t.\mathrm{ad}}=C_t\sqrt{\left(\frac{T_{t.\mathrm{ad}}}{T_t}\right)},$$

and therefore

$$T_{t.\mathrm{ad}}=T^*_{t.\mathrm{ad}}-\frac{C_t^2}{2g\frac{C_p}{A}}\,\frac{T_{t.\mathrm{ad}}}{T_t}\quad. \tag{1.62}$$

If the condition that $T_{t.\mathrm{ad}}=T_t$ be observed, then it follows from equations (1.61) and (1.62) that $T^*_{t\cdot\mathrm{ad}}=T^*_t$.

As has been shown, such an assumption has relatively little effect in determining the optimum gas temperature, but, if this assumption is made generally in turbo-jet engine calculations, then it is possible to produce a considerable error in determining the specific thrust and the specific fuel consumption, and especially at high flight velocities.

We shall give only one example.

We shall take $M_H=2{\cdot}5$, $\pi^*_c=4{\cdot}0$, $\eta^*_c=0{\cdot}83$, $\eta^*_t=0{\cdot}90$, $\nu\varphi_v==0{\cdot}975$, $a=0{\cdot}887$, $\delta_\Sigma=0{\cdot}68$, and $T^*_g/T^*_H=2{\cdot}45$ ($T^*_g=1200°$K at a flight altitude of $H=11$ km).

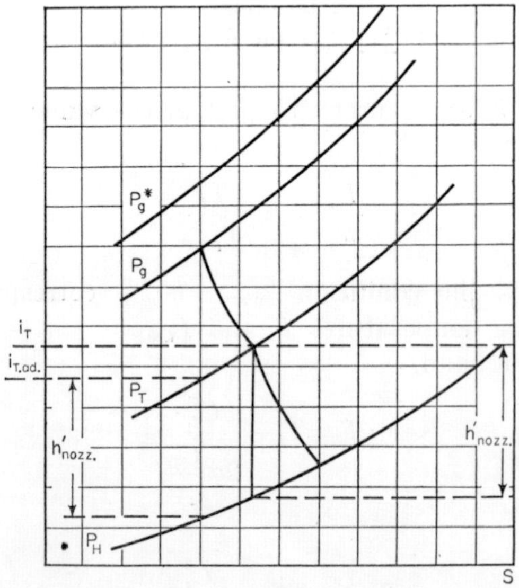

Fig. 17. Change of parameters after the turbine in an $i-S$ diagram.

For these initial data (without taking into account δ_{cool}) we obtain, if $T_t^* \neq T_{t\cdot ad}^*$, then $R_{sp}=28{\cdot}1$ kg thrust. sec/kg air and $C_R=1{\cdot}565$ kg fuel/kg thrust.hr. When $T_t^*=T_{t\cdot ad}^*$ then $R_{sp}=26{\cdot}4$ kg thrust.sec/kg air and $C_R= 1{\cdot}67$ kg fuel/kg thrust.hr. Thus, in the second case the specific fuel consumption is 5 per cent higher. and the specific thrust is correspondingly lower.

In the case when the expansion ratio is greater, the error increases.

It is necessary to pay attention to one further problem, associated with the determination of the optimum gas temperature.

All the foregoing equations were obtained for the conditions that the specific heat of the gas in the combustion chamber is constant (i.e. $B=$const.). Actually, the variation of the specific heat has an effect on the optimum gas temperature.

It follows from the expression for $C_{R\,\text{flight}}$ that

$$\frac{C_R}{\sqrt{(T_H^*)}} = C_{R_{\text{flight}}} B.$$

Differentiating this equation with respect to T_g^* and assuming that $T_H^*=$ const. we obtain

$$\left(\frac{C_R}{\sqrt{(T_H^*)}}\right)' = BC'_{R_{\text{flight}}} + C_{R_{\text{flight}}} B' . \qquad (1.63)$$

Putting $C_R/\sqrt{(T_H^*)}'=0$, we obtain from equation (1.63)

$$C'_{R_{\text{flight}}} = -C_{R_{\text{flight}}} \frac{B'}{B}.$$

The partial derivative of B with respect to T_g^* is positive. Therefore $C'_{R\,\text{flight}}<0$.

Consequently, when C_R is a minimum, then $C_{R\,\text{flight}}$ will not be a minimum but there should be a minimum at a higher gas temperature.

Figure 18 shows the variation of the optimum gas temperature at constant and variable specific heat in the combustion chamber as a function of the expansion ratio.

In accordance with what has been said, the optimum gas temperature for constant specific heat is higher than for variable specific heat, and ΔT amounts to $\sim 50°$K. The expansion ratio has a negligible effect on the temperature difference.

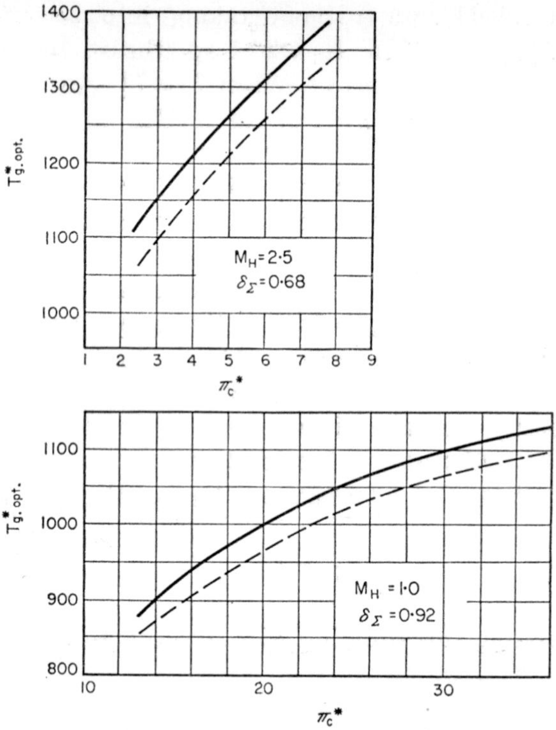

Fig. 18. Variation of optimum gas temperature, taking into account and without taking into account the variation of specific heat in the combustion chamber for $\eta_c^* = 0{\cdot}83$, $\eta_t^* = 0{\cdot}90$ and $\varphi_x = 0{\cdot}975$.

——— without taking into account variation of C_P,

— — — taking into account variation of C_P.

However, in connection with the fact that the change of the curve C_R in the minimum region is sloping, the error in determining $C_{R\,\min}$ by means of the gas temperature, derived without taking into account the variation in the specific heat, will be small in the combustion chamber.

According to the extent of increase of temperature of the gas and the flight velocity, the effect of variable specific heat on the lines of compression and expansion should become more appreciable. In order to assess this effect, calculations were carried out with respect to determining the optimum gas temperature, the optimum expansion ratio and the corresponding values of C_R. The calculations were carried out for definite representative processes of compression and expansion by means of successive approximation[1]. The results of these calculations are depicted in Figs. 19 and 20.

It follows from the graphs that the minimum values of C_R, taking into account the variation of specific heat are obtained higher, but the optimum values of T_g^* and π_c^* are reduced in comparison with their values obtained with constant specific heat on the lines of compression and expansion.

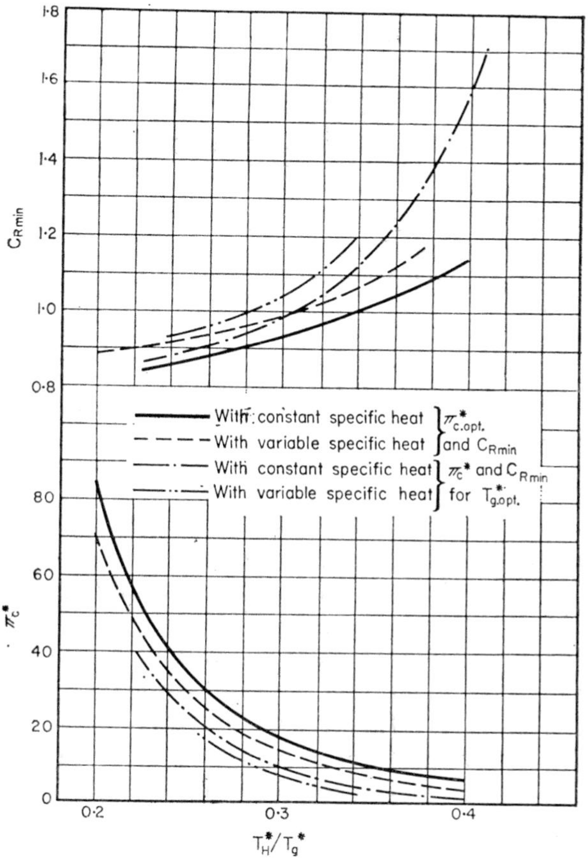

Fig. 19. Comparison of the optimum values of π_c^*, T_g^* and $C_{R\min}$ with and without taking into account the variation of specific heat on the lines of compression and expansion for $M_H = 1{\cdot}0$, $\eta_c^* = 0{\cdot}83$, $\eta^* = 0{\cdot}91$ and $\delta_\Sigma = 0{\cdot}92$.

[1] Other methods of calculation with variable specific heats are also known.

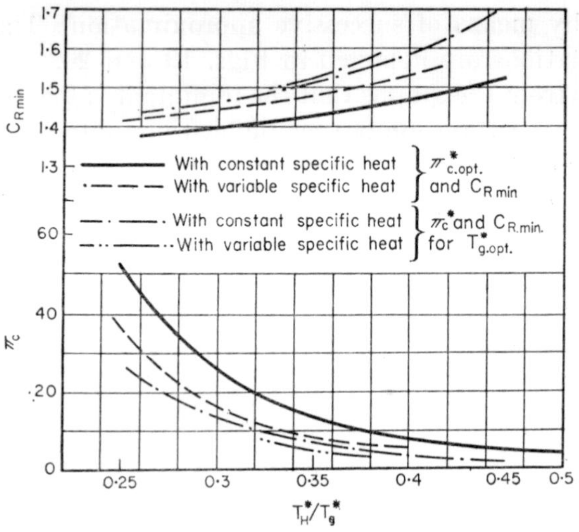

Fig. 20. Comparison of optimum values of π_c^*, T_g^* and $C_{R\min}$ with and without taking into account the variation of specific heat on the lines of compression and expansion for $M_H = 2{\cdot}5$, $\eta_c^* = 0{\cdot}83$, $\eta_t^* = 0{\cdot}91$, $\delta_\Sigma = 0{\cdot}70$ and $H \geqslant 11$ km.

However, the general regularity of the variation of the optimum values of the gas temperature and of the expansion ratio is sufficiently closely maintained in both the cases considered.

Derivation and Analysis of the Equation for determining the Expansion Ratio corresponding to Maximum Specific Thrust

The specific thrust characterizes the extent of utilization of the air which enters the engine for creating thrust.

The specific thrust is a function of those parameters upon which the specific fuel consumption also depends, see equation (1.39), excluding the coefficient B, assuming variable specific heat in the combustion chamber.

For fixed values of λ_H, T_H, efficiency and pressure coefficients the maximum value for the specific thrust should be determined by the equation

$$\frac{\partial R_{sp}}{\partial \pi_c^*} = 0 \quad \text{and} \quad \frac{\partial R_{sp}}{\partial T_g^*} = 0.$$

However, the partial derivative of R_{sp} with respect to T_g^* cannot be equal to zero, since R_{sp} increases monotonically with increase of T_g^*. Therefore only the first equation is left, from which the expansion ratio can be found which guaran tees, for specified values of the gas temperature, flight velocity and flight altitude and all efficiencies, the maximum specific thrust.

A number of authors[1] give a solution of this equation, but with the usual assumptions.

Let us find a more accurate solution with a view to verifying the known formulae. For this, as previously, we shall not assume variable specific heats in the compression and expansion processes.

The formula for specific thrust has the form

$$R_{sp}=\sqrt{(T_H^*)}\left(\nu\varphi_V\sqrt{\left\{\frac{T_t^*}{T_H^*}R\right\}(\pi_n)}-1{\cdot}87\lambda_H\right).$$

Differentiating this equation and equating to zero, we obtain

$$\left[\sqrt{\left\{\frac{T_t^*}{T_H^*}R\right\}(\pi_n)}\right]'=0$$

or

$$\frac{R'(\pi_n)}{R(\pi_n)}=-\frac{\left(\sqrt{\left\{\frac{T_t^*}{T_H^*}\right\}}\right)'}{\sqrt{(T_t^*/T_H^*)}}.$$

We shall take the derivatives with respect to $l\ (\pi_c^*)$ and therefore we shall utilize the expressions obtained previously (see p. 48.) Hence,

$$\frac{(\pi_n{}^{(k_g-1)/k_g}}{2(\pi_n{}^{2(k_g-1)/k_g}-\pi_n{}^{(k_g-1)/k_g})}=\frac{a}{2(T_t^*/T_H^*)} \tag{1.64}$$

and

$$\pi_n{}^{(k_g-1)/k_g}=-b\frac{a}{\eta_t^*(T_g^*/T_H^*)}+\pi_n{}^{(k_g-1)/k_g}\frac{k_g-1}{k_g}\,\frac{k}{k-1}\,\frac{\eta_c^*}{\pi_c^{*(k-1)/k}}. \tag{1.64a}$$

Substituting the derivative $(\pi_n{}^{(k_g-1)/k_g})$ in equation (1.64), after transformation and simplification we obtain the following equation for determining the optimum expansion ratio which guarantees maximum specific thrust:

[1] B. S. Stechkin, P. K. Kazandzhan, A. P. Alekseyev, A. N. Govorov, N. E. Konovalov, N. N. Nechayev, R. M. Fedorov, *Theory of Jet Propulsion Engines*, parts I and II, edited by B. S. Stechkin, Oborongiz, 1954. I. V. Inozemtsev, *Aircraft Gas-turbine Engines*, Oborongiz, 1955. I. I. Kulagin, *Theory of Aircraft Gas-turbine Engines*, Oborongiz, 1955.

$$(\delta_{\Sigma}\pi_c^*\pi_V)^{(k_g-1)/k_g} = \frac{\dfrac{k_g-1}{k_g}\,\dfrac{k}{k-1}\,\dfrac{\eta_c^*}{\pi_c^{*(k-1)/k}} - \dfrac{a}{\eta_t^*\dfrac{T_{t.\mathrm{ad}}^*}{T_H^*}} + \dfrac{a}{T_t^*/T_H^*}}{a(T_H^*/T_g^*)(T_{t\cdot\mathrm{ad}}^*/T_t^*)}. \quad (1.65)$$

If it be assumed admissible that

$$\frac{a}{\eta_t^* T_{\mathrm{ad}}^*/T_H^*} = \frac{a}{T_t^*/T_H^*}$$

then

$$\frac{T_{t.\mathrm{ad}}^*}{T_t^*} = \frac{1}{\eta_t^*}.$$

After this substitution we obtain the well-known equation for determining the optimum expansion ratio which is cited, in different variations, in the works mentioned above.

$$\pi_{c\,\mathrm{opt}}^* = \left[\frac{k_g-1}{k_g}\,\frac{k}{k-1}\,\frac{T_g^*}{T_H^*}\,\frac{\eta_c^*\eta_t^*}{a(\delta_{\Sigma}\pi_V)^{(k_g-1)/k_g}}\right]^{\frac{1}{(k_g-1)/k_g+(k-1)/k}} \quad (1.66)$$

We note that the assumption made leads to a physically impossible relationship

$$T_{t.\mathrm{ad}}^* > T_t^*.$$

Therefore, it is obvious that the equality of the terms

$$\frac{a}{\eta_t^*(T_{t.\mathrm{ad}}^*/T_H)} \quad \text{and} \quad \frac{a}{T_t^*/T_H^*}$$

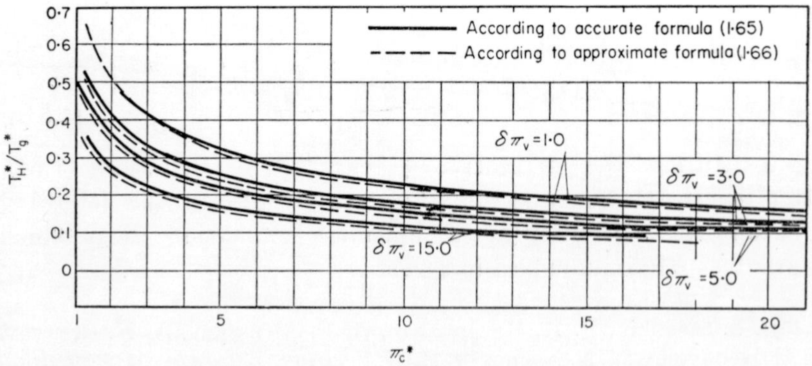

Fig. 21. Comparison of the optimum values of π_c^* corresponding to R_{spmax}, according to the accurate and the approximate formulae for $\eta_c^* = 0{\cdot}83$, $\eta_t^* = 0{\cdot}91$.

can only be for $\eta_t^* = 1{\cdot}0$. In this case the efficiency of the turbine should not enter into the simplified formula. However, in consequence of the fact that η_t^* is close to unity, the difference between the results calculated according to formulae (1.65) and (1.66) is small.

Figure 21 depicts the results of calculations carried out according to the accurate and to the approximate formulae.

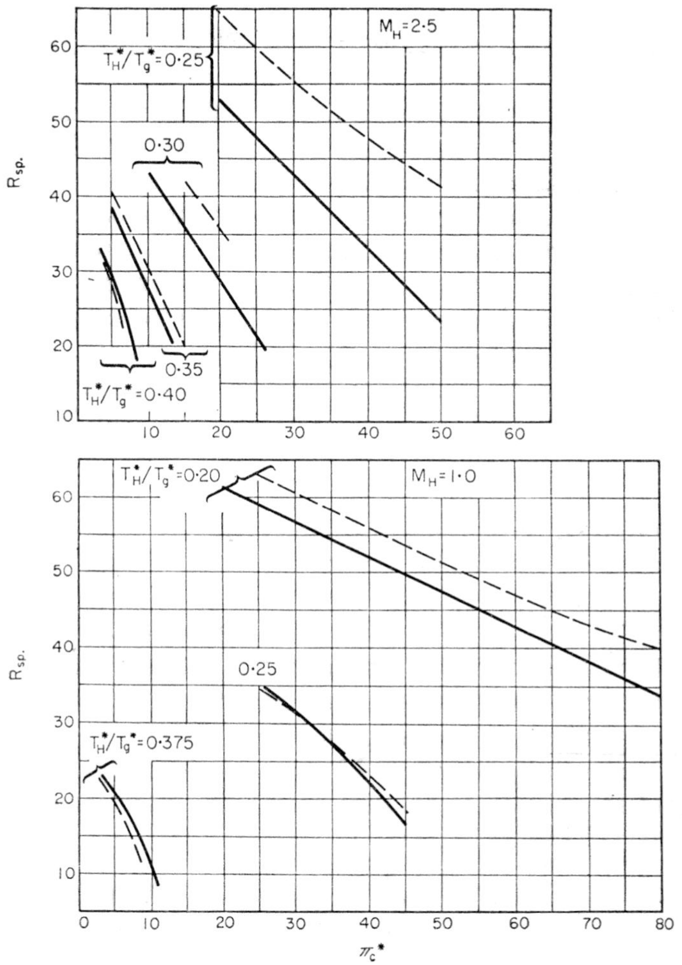

Fig. 22. Comparison of specific thrusts of turbo-jet engines, with and without taking into account variable specific heat on the lines of compression and expansion for $H = 11$ km.
——— with constant specific heat.
— — — with variable specific heat.

It can be seen from Fig. 21 that the curves, computed according to both formulae, are equidistant and approach extremely close one to the other.

Only in the region where these curves become very steep can a noticeable difference in $\pi^*_{c.\mathrm{opt}}$ be obtained for a given value of T^*_H/T^*_g, which, however, is of no significant value for practical application.

Comparison of Fig. 21 with Figs. 12 and 13 shows that the expansion ratio, optimum with respect to specific thrust, is considerably less than the expansion ratio optimum with respect to specific (fuel) consumption. This situation is well-known and is theoretically explained in the previously mentioned works of B. S. Stechkin *et al.*, N. V. Inozemtsev and I. I. Kulagin. The variation of specific heat in the compression and expansion processes may have a considerable effect on the specific thrust at high expansion ratios and with a high gas temperature (Fig. 22). It follows from Fig. 22, in particular, that the specific thrust, taking into account variable specific heat, markedly exceeds (by $\sim$5 per cent and more) R_{sp} for constant specific heat, commencing with a gas temperature of 1300 – 1400° K ($T^*_H/T^*_g=0{\cdot}2$ for $M_H=1{\cdot}0$ and $T^*_H/T^*_g=0{\cdot}35$ for $M_H=2{\cdot}5$).

Some Special Features of the Variation of R_{sp} and C_R in Turbo-jet Engines with a Reheat Chamber

A turbo-jet engine with a reheat chamber is characterized by the fact that the temperature of the gas in the jet pipe is a parameter which can be assumed to be independent of the expansion ratio and, of the temperature of the gas prior to the turbine.

If we denote the temperature of the gas in the jet pipe at the beginning of the reheat chamber by T^*_Φ, we can write down the expression for the specific thrust in the form

$$R_{\mathrm{sp}}=\sqrt{(T^*_H)}\left(\nu\varphi_V\sqrt{\left\{\frac{T^*_\Phi}{T^*_H}R\right\}(\pi_n)}-1{\cdot}87\lambda^H\right). \tag{1.67}$$

If it be assumed that ν, φ_V, T^*_Φ, T^*_H and λ_H are constants, then the maximum specific thrust will be achieved for the condition that the partial derivative of $R\,(\pi_n)$ with respect to π^*_c or to T^*_g is equal to zero, i.e. $R\,(\pi_n)'=0$ or for total expansion

$$(\pi_n{}^{(k_g-1)/k_g})'=0.$$

The partial derivative of $\pi_n{}^{(k_g-1)/k_g}$ with respect to T_g^* or T_H^*/T_g^* is expressed by the equation

$$(\pi_n{}^{(k_g-1)/k_g})'\left(\frac{T_H^*}{T_g^*}\right) = -\,(\delta_\Sigma \pi_c^* \pi_V)^{(k_g-1)/k_g}\,\frac{l(\pi_c^*)}{\eta_t^*}\,a.$$

Thus, this derivative does not depend upon T_H^*/T_g^* and consequently there is no maximum for the specific thrust of a turbo-jet engine with reheat chamber as a function of the gas temperature prior to the turbine. With increase of the gas temperature prior to the turbine for a fixed value of T_Φ^*, the specific thrust should be increased monotonically in consequence of the increase in π_n^*, whilst the temperature of the gas after the turbine T_t^* does not attain the value T_Φ^*. In connection with the fact that the temperature of the gas in the reheat chamber T_Φ^* is usually high, the condition $T_t^*=T_\Phi^*$ is practically unattainable.

Together with this it should be noted that an increase of $R\,(\pi_n)$ occurs intensively only in the region of relatively small values of π_n (see Fig. 1) and is slowed down in the region of high values of π_n. Therefore, an increase of specific thrust for an increase in T_g^* will be gradually reduced in relation to the variation of $R\,(\pi_n)$ as a function of π_n.

However, as shown below, with increase of the temperature of the gas prior to the turbine the possibility appears of increasing the efficiency factor of the compressor and reducing the dimensions of the compressor and of the turbine, which may be a supplementary reason for utilizing the high gas temperature prior to the turbine in a turbo-jet engine with reheat chamber.

On the basis of the conclusions cited above[1], the partial derivative of $\pi_n{}^{(k_g-1)/k_g}$ with respect to $l\,(\pi_c^*)$ is expressed by the equation

$$(\pi_n{}^{(k_g-1)/k_g})'\,l(\pi_c^*) = -\,(\delta_\Sigma \pi_c^* \pi_V)^{(k_g-1)/k_g}\,\frac{a}{\eta_t^*(T_g^*/T_H^*)} + \\ +\pi_n{}^{(k_g-1)/k_g}\,\frac{k_g-1}{k_g}\;\frac{k}{k-1}\;\frac{\eta_c^*}{\pi_c^{*(k-1)/k}}.$$

We shall substitute in this equation $\pi_n{}^{(k_g-1)/k_g}$ by the following expression:

[1] In these conclusions and below, it is assumed that there is no difference between the values of kg for the expansion process in the turbine and in the jet pipe.

$$\pi_n{}^{(k_g-1)/k_g} = (\delta_\Sigma \pi_c^* \pi_V)^{(k_g-1)/k_g}\left(1 - a\frac{T_H^*}{T_g^*}\frac{l(\pi_c)}{\eta_t^*}\right).$$

After substitution and transformation we obtain the equation for the expansion ratio at which the maximum thrust is attained in an engine with a reheat chamber:

$$\pi_c^{*(k-1)/k} = \frac{1 + a\dfrac{T_H^*}{T_g^*}\dfrac{1}{\eta_c^*\eta_t^*}}{a\dfrac{T_H^*}{T_g^*}\dfrac{1}{\eta_c^*\eta_t^*}\left(1 + \dfrac{k_g}{k_g-1}\dfrac{k-1}{k}\right)}. \qquad (1.68)$$

The same formula is obtained also for incomplete expansion.

It follows from the equation obtained that the optimum expansion ratio depends, primarily, on T_H^*/T_g^* and the product of the efficiencies of the compressor and of the turbine.

Figure 23 shows the dependence of π_c^*, corresponding to maximum specific thrust, on T_H^*/T_g^*. For the calculations it has been taken that $a = 0{\cdot}887$ and $k_g = 1{\cdot}33$. From comparison of the curves presented in Figs. 21 and 23 it can be seen that in an engine with a reheat chamber the expansion ratio, corresponding to maximum specific thrust, is considerably higher than in a turbo-jet engine without reheat chamber and particularly in the region of small values of T_H^*/T_g^*.

However, the curve of specific thrust for a turbo-jet engine with reheat chamber varies, in the vicinity of the extremum, with a steep slope (Fig. 24) and therefore a significant deviation from the optimum value of π_c^* will not exert a substantial effect on the magnitude of the specific thrust.

At the same time it should be noted that the use in a turbo-jet engine with reheat chamber of a higher expansion ratio limits the output of the compressor less at high supersonic flight velocities; this is considered in more detail below. Moreover, in the case of using a given engine without a reheat chamber, it will have a worse efficiency at a higher expansion ratio. Finally, at one and the same temperature T_Φ^*, the increase in thrust as a result of switching in the reheat chamber will be greater in the case of increased values of π_c^* as a consequence of the increase in the extent of preheating.

Let us consider the problem concerning the specific fuel consumption in a turbo-jet engine with reheat chamber. Denoting the ratio of the fuel consumption to the air flow rate for the main chamber

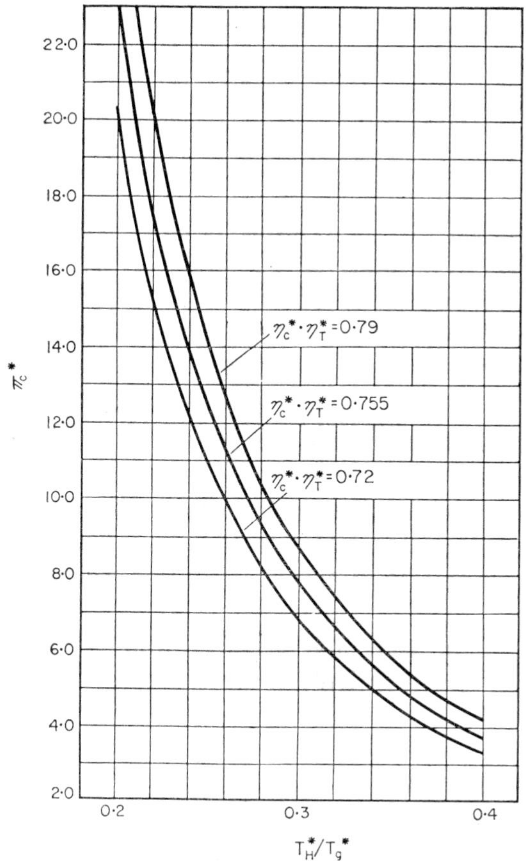

Fig 23. Dependence of π_c^*, corresponding to maximum specific thrust of a turbo-jet engine with reheat chamber, on T_H^*/T_g^* for different values of $\eta_c^*\eta_t^*$.

by q_1, and the ratio of the fuel to the gas flow rate for the reheat chamber by q_2, we can write

$$C_R = 3600\,\frac{G_{a.c}q_1 + G_g q_2}{G_a R_{sp}} = 3600\,\frac{G_a \delta_{cool} q_1 + G_a \nu_1 q_2}{G_a R_{sp}}$$

or

$$C_R = \frac{\delta_{cool} q_{01} + \nu_1 q_{02}}{R_{sp}},$$

where

$$q_{01} = 3600\, q_1 \text{ and } q_{02} = 3600\, q_2.$$

The value of q_{01} can be expressed by the equation

$$q_{01}=B\,(T_g^*-T_k^*).$$

Similarly, the equation for q_{02} can also be written:

$$q_{02}=B_1\,(T_\Phi^*-T_t^*).$$

In order to evaluate the coefficient B_1 it is also possible to use equation (1.33), if, in place of T_g^* and T_k^*, the temperatures T_Φ^* and T_t^* are used, and the specific heats corresponding to them, taking into consideration the mixture composition.

Thus, the expression for C_R takes the form

$$C_R=\frac{\delta_{cool}B(T_g^*-T_k^*)+\nu_1 B_1(T^*-T_t^*)}{R_{sp}}\,. \qquad (1.69)$$

In order to establish, with a certain approximation, the conditions for which the specific fuel consumption in a turbo-jet engine with reheat chamber will be minimum, we shall make a number of assumptions.

We shall assume that $\delta_{cool}=\nu_1=1{\cdot}0$ and $B=B_1=B_{av}$.

Moreover, in the equation for the balance of the powers of the compressor and of the turbine we shall assume that

$$\frac{G_a}{G_g}\;\frac{\dfrac{k}{k-1}R}{\dfrac{k_g}{k_g-1}R_g\eta_m}=1{\cdot}0.$$

Hence

$$T_g^*-T_t^*=T_k^*-T_H^*.$$

Introducing all the assumptions mentioned into equation (1.69), we obtain

$$C_R=\frac{B_{av}(T_\Phi^*-T_H^*)}{R_{sp}}\,. \qquad (1.70)$$

It can be seen from this equation that for constant values of T_Φ^*, T_H^* and B_{av}, the minimum value of C_R applies in the case when the specific thrust attains a maximum, and consequently an expansion ratio is achieved corresponding to equation (1.68). In connection with the sloping course of the specific thrust curve in the region of extremum, the specific fuel consumption will also vary slightly for values of $\pi^* \leqslant \pi^*_{c\,opt}$, which, in its turn also justifies the assumptions made above. This is also verified by the data presented in Fig. 24.

With increase of the temperature of the gas in the reheat chamber, for approximately equal conditions, the efficiency of the turbo-jet engine with reheat will be worsened, since the fuel consumption increases more rapidly than the specific thrust, which can be seen from equations (1.67) and (1.70).

An increase in the flight velocity, as is well-known, has a favourable effect on the efficiency of a turbo-jet engine with reheat, which is a consequence of an increase in the overall as well as in the effective efficiency of the engine.

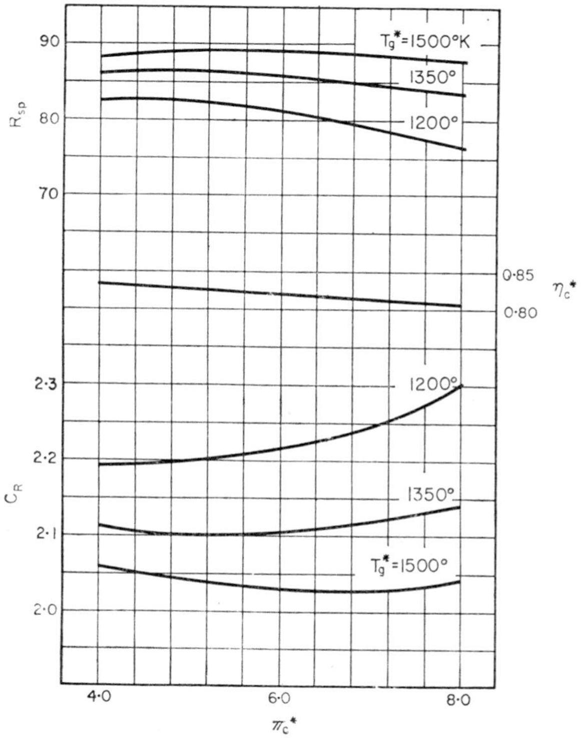

Fig. 24. Dependence of specific thrust and specific fuel consumption of a turbo-jet engine with reheat chamber on π^*_c and T^*_g for $M^*_H = 2{\cdot}5$; H $\geqslant$ 11,000 m; $T^*_\Phi = 2000°$ K.

CHAPTER II

Basis of Selection of Engine Parameters for Rated Flight Conditions, Taking into Account Aerodynamic and Design Data for the Compressor and Turbine

General Aspects

In selecting the expansion ratio and gas temperature for rated flight conditions, designers inevitably encounter the opposing influences of these basic parameters on the efficiency, dimensional and weight data of an engine.

As was shown in Chapter I, an increase in the expansion ratio leads to a gain in efficiency of the engine, but at the same time the specific thrust is reduced, which, in the general case, is associated with an increase in the dimensions of the engine.

An increase in the gas temperature increases the specific thrust, but reduces the efficiency of the engine, if the value of π_c^* is not increased relative to the increase in the gas temperature.

In an engine rated for a high supersonic flight velocity and utilizing a high temperature reheat chamber, the effect of the expansion ratio and of the gas temperature prior to the turbine on the specific thrust and on the specific fuel consumption is, as was shown above, relatively small, as a consequence of which the impression may be created that it is advantageous to use high values of T_g^* and π_c^* in these engines.

It is shown below that the problem mentioned can be narrowed down by linking up the engine parameters T_g^* and π_c^* not only with its thermodynamic characteristics C_R and R_{sp} but also with certain gas – dynamic and design factors and, in particular, with the peripheral speed and output of the compressor, and also with the stability and output of the turbine.

The Relationship connecting Engine Parameters and Flight Conditions with Stable Turbine Data, Output and Peripheral Speed of the Compressor

The output of a compressor can be assessed by means of the efficiency coefficient, which represents the ratio of the actual air flow rate through the inlet section of the compressor to the flow rate attainable for the critical parameters and the relative diameter of the hub of the first stage $d=0$:

$$\overline{G}_c = \frac{G_a}{G_{a0}}.$$

Since

$$G_a = \frac{p_a^* F_a q(\lambda_a) S}{\sqrt{(T_a^*)}} \sin\alpha_a \text{ and } G_{a0} \frac{p_a^* F_{a0} S}{\sqrt{(T_a^*)}}, \text{ then}$$

$$\overline{G}_c = \frac{G_a}{G_{a0}} = q(\lambda_a) \frac{F_a}{F_{a0}} \sin\alpha_a .$$

Since $F_a \frac{\pi D_c^2}{4}(1-\overline{d}^2)$ and $F_{a0} = \frac{\pi D_c^2}{4}$ then finally

$$\overline{G}_c = q(\lambda_a)(1-\overline{d}^2)\sin\alpha_a.$$

The efficiency coefficient can be linked with the rotational speed of the compressor, since

$$n_c = \frac{60 u_c}{\pi D_c} \text{ and } D_k^2 = \frac{4 G_a \sqrt{(T_a^*)}}{\pi S p_a^* \overline{G}_c}.$$

Assuming that for air $S=0{\cdot}396$, we obtain[1]

$$u_c^2 \overline{G}_c = n_c^2 \frac{G_a \sqrt{(T_H^*)}}{113{\cdot}4 p_a^*}. \tag{2.1}$$

It can be seen from this equation that for a given driving air flow rate, the selection of the peripheral speed and the efficiency coefficient depends on the attainable number of revolutions of the compressor. If the r. p. m. of the compressor is unlimited, then the maximum attainable values for the peripheral speed and compressor output can be assumed. Otherwise, one of these parameters is inevitably limited.

[1] In future, the symbol T_H^* will be used in place of T_a^*, since $T_a^* = T_H^*$.

The r.p.m. of the compressor may be limited by the stresses on the turbine blades. As a result of this the level of attainable rotational speed will be determined, primarily, by the tensile stresses from the centrifugal forces, since these stresses are the greatest. Moreover, the buckling stresses from the force of the gas may change on account of the width of the blade, and also it is partially or wholly compensated by the buckling stresses from the centrifugal forces.

As shown below, the tensile stresses can be expressed not only as a function of the rotational speed and design data of the blades, but also as a function of the supply and gas-dynamic parameters of the gas on discharge from the turbine. This enables, for a given stress, the connection between the attainable speed and the basic parameters of the engine T_g^* and π_c^* to be established, which is used in the present work.

The tensile stresses

$$\sigma_{pi} = \frac{\gamma_b}{g}\,\omega^2 \frac{\int_{r_i}^{r_t} rF\mathrm{d}r}{F_i} \tag{2.2}$$

where σ_{pi} and F_i are the tensile stresses and the area of cross-section at a certain radius r_i;

γ_b is the specific gravity of the blade material;

ω is the angular velocity;

r_t is the radius of the tip section of the blade;

F and r are variables of integration ($r_i \leqslant r \leqslant r_t$).

It follows from formula (2.2) that the tensile stresses are independent of the absolute dimensions of the cross-sectional area of the blade.

For a blade with constant cross-sectional area with respect to height, the maximum tensile stress will arise near the root of the blade:

$$\sigma_{p0} = 2\frac{\gamma_b}{g}\,u_{av}^2 \frac{1}{D_{av}/h}, \tag{2.3}$$

where u_{av} is the peripheral speed at the mean radius;

D_{av} is the mean diameter of the blade;

h is the height of the blade.

Equation (2.3) can be written in another form:

$$\sigma_{p0} = \frac{\gamma_b}{g}\,u_t^2 \frac{1-\bar{d}_t^2}{2}. \tag{2.4}$$

where u_t is the peripheral speed at the outer radius;
d_t is the relative diameter of the turbine hub.

Between the quantity D_{av}/h, by means of which is characterized the relative height (length) of the blade, and the relative diameter of the hub there exist the relationships

$$\frac{D_{av}}{h} = \frac{1+\bar{d}_t}{1-\bar{d}_t} \text{ and } \bar{d}_t = \frac{(D_{av}/h)-1}{(D_{av}/h)+1}.$$

The minimum value of D_{av}/h nowadays amounts to three (in the latter stages of the turbines of turbo-jet engines). In this case $\bar{d}_t = 0{\cdot}5$.

In modern turbines of turbo-jet engines, the magnitudes of D_{av}/h and $\bar{d}_t$ are considerably higher.

For a blade with some other law of variation of cross-sectional area with respect to height of the blade, the maximum stresses can be written in the form

$$\sigma_p = \sigma_{p0}\Phi, \tag{2.5}$$

where σ_{p0} is the stress in the tip section of a blade of constant cross-section for the same $\gamma_b u_{av}$ and D_{av}/h;
Φ is the shape factor.

The value of the shape factor Φ depends on the type of blade. It is most important to note that for an accepted design principle for the blade with a given ratio of the cross-sectional area at the tip to the cross-sectional area at the base, $\chi = F(r_t)/F(r_0)$, the shape factor depends slightly on the ratio D_{av}/h or on the relative diameter of the hub $\bar{d}_t$.

This circumstance enables a relative assessment of a turbo-jet engine to be made in the present section.

This circumstance enables one to assume an identical value for Φ in the present section, for a relative assessment of turbo-jet engines with different turbines, even though with respect to the magnitude of D_{av}/h or d_t these turbines may differ considerably.

Figure 25 shows, according to data by I. A. Birger, the dependence of Φ_{on} $\bar{d}_t$ for blades with an area of cross-section varying according to a linear law.

Figures 26 and 27 show the dependence of Φ on d_t respectively for exponential blades and for blades with a cross-sectional area varying according to a power law (for the power index, $x=2$ and 3).

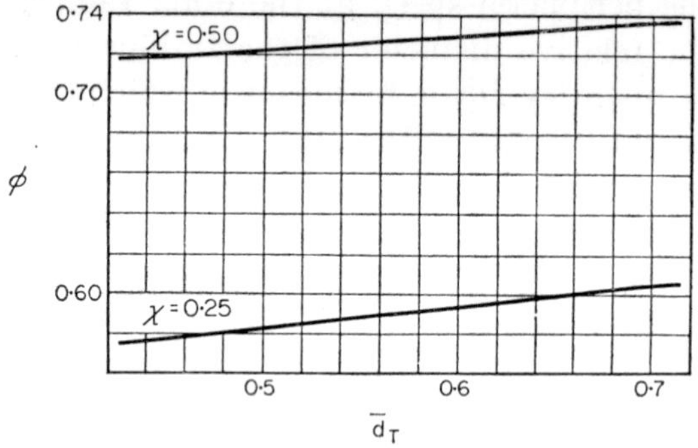

Fig. 25. Dependence of Φ on $\overline{d_t}$ for blades with an area of cross-section varying according to a linear law.

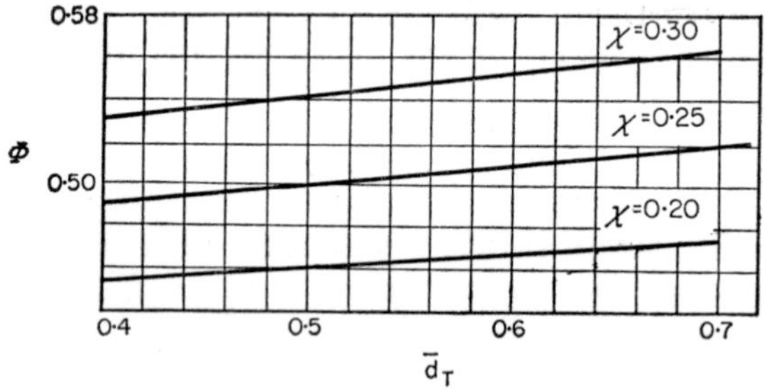

Fig. 26. Dependence of Φ on $\overline{d_t}$ for exponential blades.

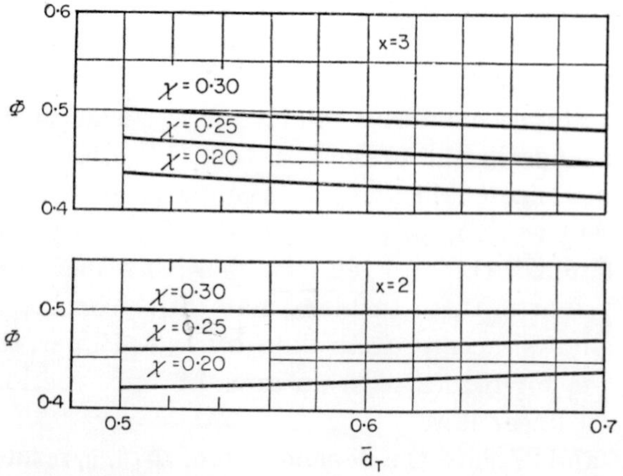

Fig. 27. Dependence of Φ on $\overline{d_t}$ for blades with a cross-sectional area varying according to a power law.

For cases in which the maximum stress occurs in the intermediate cross-section, the shape factor Φ refers to this section.

The curves depicted in Figs. 25, 26 and 27 confirm the small effect of $\bar{d}_t$ noted above. It can also be seen from these figures that for a value of $\chi = 0{\cdot}25 \sim$, corresponding to an average modern turbine, the shape factor Φ, within the range of values for $\bar{d}_t$ from 0·5 to 0·7 is equal to $\Phi = 0{\cdot}58 - 0{\cdot}60$ for blades in which the cross-sectional area varies according to a linear law, $\Phi = 0{\cdot}50 - 0{\cdot}52$ for exponential blades, $\Phi = 0{\cdot}45 - 0{\cdot}47$ for blades in which the cross-sectional area varies according to a power law.

If the stress σ_{p0} is expressed via the r.p.m., then equation (2.5) assumes the form

$$\sigma_p = 2\frac{\gamma_b}{g}\frac{\pi^2}{60}n_t^2 D_{av} h\Phi \,. \qquad (2.6)$$

If it be assumed that the mean diameter is determined according to the discharge rim, then the product $D_{av}h$ can be substituted by the circular area F_t on discharge from the turbine, arising from the relationship $D_{av}h = F_t/\pi$.

Assuming also that $\gamma_b = 8{\cdot}4 \times 10^3$ kg/m³, we obtain σ_p expressed in kg/m². Dividing it by 10^4, we obtain σ_p expressed in kg/cm²:

$$\sigma_p = 1{\cdot}5 \times 10^{-4} n_t^2 F_t. \qquad (2.7)$$

Substituting the discharge area of the turbine by the flow rate and mean parameters of the gas in the discharge section, we obtain

$$\sigma_p = 3{\cdot}86 \times 10^{-4} n_t^2 \frac{G_{g.t}\sqrt{(T_t^*)}}{p_t^* q(\lambda_t)\sin\alpha_t}\Phi \,, \qquad (2.8)$$

where p_t^* is expressed in kg/m².

Hence

$$n_t^2 = \frac{\sigma_p p_t^*}{3{\cdot}86 \times 10^{-4}}\,\frac{q(\lambda_t)\sin\alpha_t}{G_{g.t}\sqrt{(T_b^*\Phi)}} \,. \qquad (2.9)$$

If we compare the number of revolutions of the compressor and of the turbine and if we substitute

$$\frac{G_{g.t}}{G_a} = \nu_t,\; p_t^* = \frac{\delta_g p_k^*}{\pi_t^*},\; \frac{p_k^*}{p_a^*} = \pi_c^*,$$

then

$$\frac{u_c^2 G_c}{\sigma_p q(\lambda_t)} = \frac{\sin\alpha_t \delta_g \pi_c^* \sqrt{(T_H^*)}}{0{\cdot}0439\nu_t \Phi\sqrt{(T_t^*)}\pi^*_t} \,. \qquad (2.9a)$$

We express the values of T_g^* and π_t^* via T_g^* and π_c^* by means of the equation of power balance of the compressor and turbine Then the previous equation assumes the form

$$\frac{u_c^2 G_c}{\sigma_p q(\lambda_t)} = \frac{\sin\alpha_t \delta_g \pi_c^* \sqrt{\left(\frac{T_H^*}{T_g^*}\right)\left(1 - a\frac{T_H^*}{T_g^*}\,\frac{\pi_c^{*(k-1)/k} - 1}{\eta_k^* \eta_t^*}\right)^{k_g/(k_g-1)}}}{0{\cdot}0439 \nu_t \Phi \sqrt{\left(1 - a(T_H^*/T_g^*)\frac{\pi_c^{*(k-1)/k} - 1}{\eta_c^*}\right)}} \qquad (2.10)$$

This equation in the generalized form connects together the basic design and gas-dynamic data of the compressor (u_c and G_c) and of the turbine [σ_p, $q(\lambda_t)$] with the engine parameters. For this, it is important to note that the gas temperature enters into this equation in the form of the ratio T_H^*/T_g^* and, consequently, the effect of the gas temperature is connected with the altitude and flight speed. The tensile stresses correspond to the blades of the last stage of the turbine. The relationship between the stresses in different stages is discussed below.

Assuming that the coefficients in the first part of the equation are constants, we obtain the functional relationship

$$\frac{u_c^2 G_c}{\sigma_p q(\lambda_t)} = f\left(\pi_c^*, \frac{T_H^*}{T_g^*}\right). \qquad (2.11)$$

Thus, to each value of π_c^* and T_H^*/T_g^* there corresponds a completely finite value of the complex parameter $u_c^2 G_c/\sigma_p q(\lambda_t)$, which we shall denote in future by the symbol Π.[1]

It is obvious that the validity is also reversible, i. e., that by choosing the values of the peripheral speed and of the output factor of the compressor, and also the tensile stress in the blades of the turbine and the velocity coefficient after the turbine, there should correspond a definite value for the expansion ratio and the gas temperature for the assumed efficiencies and specified altitude and velocity of flight. For this it should be noted that if the material of the tur-

[1] The peripheral speed of the compressor enters into the parameter Π in m/sec and the stress in kg/cm². Consequently, the quantity Π has a dimension of m²cm²/sec² kg. However, if Π is multiplied by the constant dimensional factor 0·0439 (see equation 2·10), then the quantity Π will be dimensionless. In the present work, the numerical value of Π is used for convenience presented in the dimensional form, but the dimension is conditionally omitted (similar to that which is done in the quantites $n/\sqrt{T}$; L/T; etc.).

bine blades is specified, then the values of σ_p and T_g^* should be further matched by a permissible safety factor. Such a generalized relationship reveals an inter-connection between the basic engine parameters and its various units with the flight conditions, and permits a number of important aspects to be established, as will be shown below.

It can be assumed that the complex parameter Π is a criterion of comparison for the turbo-compressor part of an engine, since its value should be one and the same for geometrically and gas – dynamically similar turbo-compressors.

However, for blades manufactured from identical material their safety factors with respect to tensile stresses will, in the general case, be different.

Figure 28 shows the change of the complex parameter Π as a function of T_H^*/T_g^* for different values of π_c^* and for the following values of the remaining coefficients:

$$\nu_t = 1{\cdot}025;\ \ \delta_g = 0{\cdot}97;\ \ \sin\alpha_t = 0{\cdot}995\ \ (\alpha_t = 84°);$$
$$\eta_c^* = 0{\cdot}83;\ \ \eta_t^* = 0{\cdot}91;\ \ \Phi = 0{\cdot}5;\ \ a = 0{\cdot}887.$$

It can be seen from Fig. 28 that commencing with a certain value of T_H^*/T_g^*, for which for a given expansion ratio $\Pi_{\max}$ is achieved, the complex parameter is reduced according to the extent of the increase in T_H^*/T_g^*. This reduction occurs more intensively at increased values of π_c^*. The reduction of the complex parameter is a consequence of the increase of the degree of expansion in the turbine. The latter is dependent upon the increase of the compression work in the compressor in the case of increase of T_H for a given gas temperature T_g^* and π_c^* or as a consequence of the necessity of guaranteeing the designated work as a result of the reduction of T_g^* and of the constant temperature of the air maintaining T_H^*, by means of increasing the expansion ratio.

Physically, the effect of an increase in π_c^* on the complex parameter is explained by the increase in the requisite straight-through area F_t at the exit from the turbine for a specified gas flow rate, on account of the reduction of its density. This leads, in the long run, to the fact that for a permissible stress in the turbine blades the possible r.p.m. is reduced, as follows from equation (2.7). As a result, the magnitude of the product $u_c^2\overline{G}_c$ is reduced (see equation 2.1) and consequently also the entire complex parameter.

Figure 29 shows the dependence of Π on π_c^* for different values of T_H^*/T_g^* and of the product $\eta_c^*\eta_t^*$. The remaining coefficients are assumed to be the same as in Fig. 28.

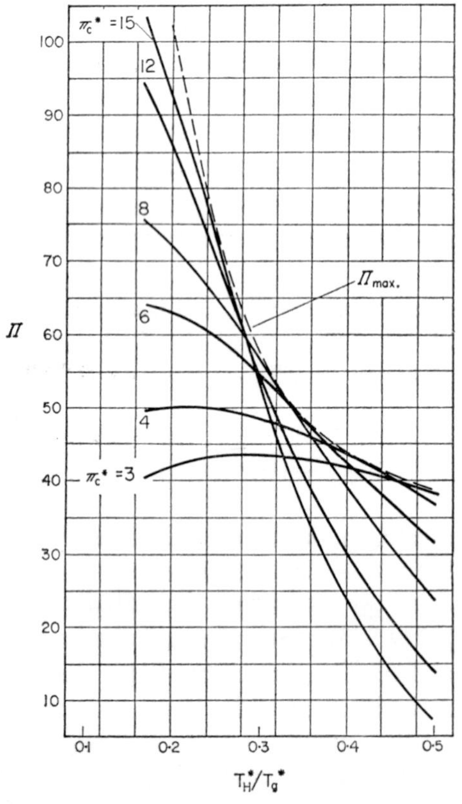

Fig. 28. Dependence of the complex parameter on T_H^*/T_g^* for different values of π_c^*.

It is advantageous to note that a change in the efficiency of the turbine has practically the same effect on the magnitude of the complex parameter as does the efficiency of the compressor. This conclusion can be drawn directly from equation (2.10), in which the products of the efficiency coefficients of the turbine and of the compressor enter into the constitution of the term raised to the fourth power, but the separate efficiency of the compressor comes under the square root sign.

If we pass over slight deviations and assume that in equation (2.10) all values, excluding η_c^* and η_t^* are constant, then

$$\frac{d\Pi}{\Pi} = K_1 \frac{d(\eta_c^* \eta_t^*)}{\eta_c^* \eta_t^*} + K_2 \frac{d\eta_c^*}{\eta_c^*},$$

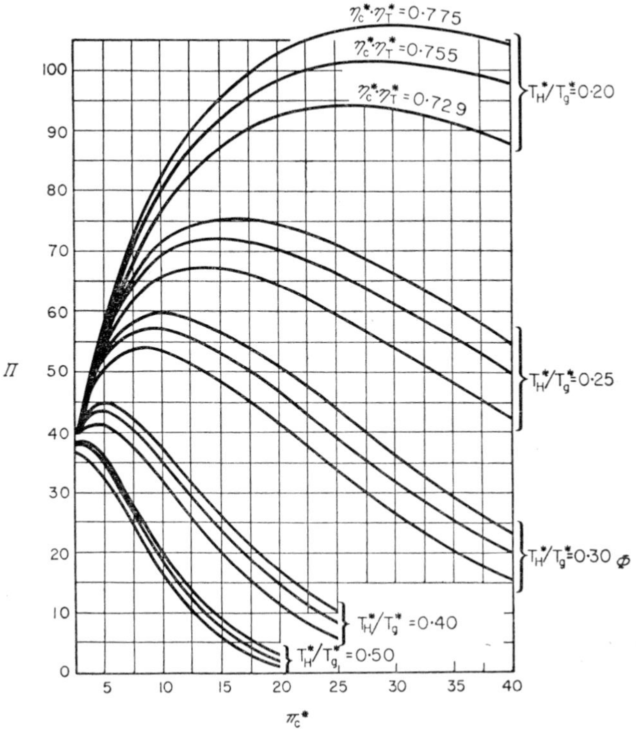

Fig. 29. Dependence of the complex parameter on π_c^* the efficiency of the compressor and the efficiency of the turbine.

where

$$K_1 = \frac{4a \frac{T_H^*}{T_g^*} \left(\pi_c^{*(k-1)/k} - 1\right)}{\left(1 - a \frac{T_H^*}{T_g^*} \frac{\pi_c^{*(k-1)/k} - 1}{\eta_t^* \eta_c^*}\right) \eta_t^* \eta_c^*};$$

$$K_2 = \frac{1}{2} \frac{a \frac{T_H^*}{T_g^*} \left(\pi_c^{*(k-1)/k} - 1\right)}{\left(1 - a \frac{T_H^*}{T_g^*} \frac{\pi_c^{*(k-1)/k} - 1}{\eta_c^*}\right) \eta_c^*}.$$

The ratio of these coefficients can be written down in the following form:

$$\frac{K_1}{K_2} \cong \frac{8}{\eta_t^*} \approx 9{\cdot}0.$$

As a consequence of the fact that K_1 is substantially greater than K_2, it can be assumed that

$$\frac{\mathrm{d}\Pi}{\Pi} = K_1 \frac{\mathrm{d}(\eta_t^* \eta_c^*)}{\eta_t^* \eta_c^*}.$$

Consequently, the change in Π is determined mainly by the product of the efficiency coefficients of the turbine and compressor independently of their absolute values.

The effect of the product $\eta^* \eta_c^*$ on Π, as is shown in Fig. 29, is fairly substantial, especially in the region of large values of π_c^* and small ratios of T_H^*/T_g^*.

For every expansion ratio there is a maximum value of the complex parameter, to which corresponds a certain value of T_H^*/T_g^*. This value of T_H^*/T_g^* can be expressed by a simple equation.

For simplification, we introduce into equation (2.10) the quantity used earlier

$$l(\pi_c^*) = \frac{\pi_c^{*(k-1)/k} - 1}{\eta_c^*}.$$

We obtain

$$\Pi = \frac{\sin \alpha_t \delta_g \pi_c^* \sqrt{\left(\frac{T_H^*}{T_g^*}\right)\left(1 - a \frac{T_H^*}{T_g^*} \frac{l(\pi_c^*)}{\eta_t^*}\right)^{\;/(\;\;-1)}}}{0{\cdot}0439 \nu_t \Phi \sqrt{\left(1 - a \frac{T_H^*}{T_g^*} l(\pi_c^*)\right)}}. \qquad (2.12)$$

We take the partial derivative of the right-hand side with respect to T_H^*/T_g^* and equate it to zero:

$$-\left[1 - a \frac{T_H^*}{T_g^*} l(\pi_c^*)\right] \frac{T_H^*}{T_g^*} \frac{\frac{k_g}{k_g - 1} a \frac{l(\pi_c^*)}{\eta_t^*}}{1 - a \frac{T_H^*}{T_g^*} \frac{l(\pi_c^*)}{\eta_t^*}} +$$

$$+ \frac{1}{2}\left[1 - a \frac{T_H^*}{T_g^*} l(\pi_c^*)\right] + \frac{T_H^*}{T_g^*} \frac{a l(\pi_c^*)}{2} = 0.$$

It can be assumed with a small error in the first term of the equation that

$$1-a\frac{T_H^*}{T_g^*}l(\pi_c^*)\cong 1-a\frac{T_H^*}{T_g^*}\frac{(\pi_c^*)}{\eta_t^*}.$$

This assumption corresponds to the equation $T_t^*=T_{t.ad}^*$ which was also adopted earlier.

By using the assumption mentioned we obtain

$$\left(\frac{T_H^*}{T_g^*}\right)_{opt}=\frac{\eta_t^*}{2\frac{k_g}{k_g-1}al(\pi_c^*)}. \tag{2.13}$$

For large values of π_c^* the ratio of (T_H^*/T_g^*) turns out to be small, which corresponds to an extremely high gas temperature. For example, even for $\pi_c^*=8{\cdot}0$, $\eta_t^*=0{\cdot}91$ and $\eta_c^*=0{\cdot}83$ we shall have $(T_H^*/T_g^*)_{opt}=0{\cdot}13$, which, for $M_H=1{\cdot}0$ and $H=11$ km corresponds to $T_{g.opt}=2000$°K.

For small values of π_c^* the ratio $(T_H^*/T_g^*)_{opt}$ may correspond to real values of T_g^*. For example, for $\pi_c^*=4{\cdot}0$ we shall have $(T_H^*/T_g^*)_{opt}=0{\cdot}218$, which for the conditions shown above corresponds to a gas temperature $T_g^*=1190$°K. However, for $M_H=2{\cdot}5$, when $T_H=490$°K, the optimum gas temperature also for $\pi_c^*=4{\cdot}0$ is unrealistically high:

$$T_{g.opt}^*=2240°\text{K}.$$

Thus, it can be assumed that for $\pi_c^*=$const. and for an increase in T_H^*/T_g^* the value of the complex parameter should be, as a rule, reduced, since the real values of T_H^*/T_g^* exceed their values corresponding to Π_{max}.

It can be seen from Fig. 29 that there is a maximum Π also for every value of T_H^*/T_g^*.

By equating to zero the derivative with respect to $l(\pi_c^*)$ of the right hand portion of equation (2.12), we obtain, after small transformations

$$-\frac{a\frac{T_H^*}{T_g^*}}{2\left[1-a\frac{T_H^*}{T_g^*}l(\pi_c^*)\right]}=\frac{\pi_c^{*\prime}}{\pi_c^*}-\frac{\pi_c^*\frac{k_g}{k_g-1}a\frac{T_H^*}{T_g^*}\frac{1}{\eta_t^*}}{\left[1-a\frac{T_H^*}{T_g^*}\frac{l(\pi_c^*)}{\eta_t^*}\right]}.$$

The ratio $\pi_c^{*\prime}/\pi_c^*$, where $\pi_c^{*\prime}$ is the derivative of π_c^* with respect to $l(\pi_c^*)$ may be written as

$$\frac{\pi_c^{*\prime}}{\pi_c^*}=\frac{k}{k-1}\,\frac{\pi_c^*}{\pi_c^{*(k-1)/k}}.$$

Substituting this relationship in the previous equation and reducing the right hand portion to the one denominator, we have

$$-\frac{\dfrac{a}{2}\,\dfrac{T_H^*}{T_g^*}}{\left[1-a\dfrac{T_H^*}{T_g^*}\,l(\pi_c^*)\right]}=$$

$$=\frac{\dfrac{k}{k-1}\,\dfrac{\eta_c^*}{\pi_c^{*(k-1)/k}}\left[1-a\dfrac{T_H^*}{T_g^*}\,\dfrac{l(\pi_c^*)}{\eta_t^*}\right]-\dfrac{k_g}{k_g-1}\,a\,\dfrac{T_H^*}{T_g^*}\,\dfrac{1}{\eta_t^*}}{\left[1-a\dfrac{T_H^*}{T_g^*}\,\dfrac{l(\pi_c^*)}{\eta_t^*}\right]}.$$

As calculations show, the denominators in the right and left portions of the equation can also be equated in this equation, with an extremely small error. We then finally obtain

$$\pi_{c\,\mathrm{opt}}^*=\left[\frac{\dfrac{k}{k-1}\left(\eta_c^*\eta_t^*+a\dfrac{T_H^*}{T_g^*}\right)}{a\dfrac{T_H^*}{T_g^*}\left(\dfrac{k}{k-1}+\dfrac{k_g}{k_g-1}-\dfrac{\eta_g^*}{2}\right)}\right]^{k/(k-1)}. \qquad (2.14)$$

This equation shows that the optimum value of π_c^*, corresponding to the maximum of the complex parameter depends only on η_t^*, η_c^* and T_H^*/T_g^*. Numerical values of $\pi_{c.\mathrm{opt}}^*$ can be seen from Fig. 29.

It is useful to note that for large values of T_H^*/T_g^*, corresponding to large flight speeds, the value of $\pi_{c.\mathrm{opt}}^*$ is relatively small and for an increase of π_c^* beyond optimum the complex parameter is strongly reduced.

Let us write equation (2.14) in the form

$$\pi_c^{*(k-1)/k}=\frac{1+a\dfrac{T_H^*}{T_g^*}\,\dfrac{1}{\eta_c^*\eta_t^*}}{a\dfrac{T_H^*}{T_g^*}\,\dfrac{1}{\eta_c^*\eta_t^*}\left(1+\dfrac{k_g}{k_g-1}\,\dfrac{k-1}{k}-\dfrac{\eta_t^*}{2^{k/(k-1)}}\right)}. \qquad (2.15)$$

Comparing this equation with equation (1.68), which gives the value of π_c^* corresponding to the maximum specific thrust in a turbo-jet engine with reheat chamber, it is not difficult to see that the equations are practically identical, since in equation (2.15) the term

$$\frac{\eta_t^*}{2\dfrac{k}{k-1}}$$

is small in comparison with the other terms in brackets.

Appraisal of Certain Special Features of Engines of a Different Type with the Aid of the Complex Parameter II

Turbo-jet engine with a single-cascade axial compressor. In order to illustrate the application of the generalized relationship we shall discuss with the aid of the complex parameter some special features of a turbo-jet engine with a single axial compressor cascade. Part of these special features will be studied in more detail later on.

In connection with the reduction in magnitude of the complex parameter as a result of an increase in T_H^*/T_g^*, which, in particular, occurs as a result of increase of flight speed, the necessity may arise at large values of M_H to limit either the peripheral speed or the output of the compressor. This in its turn is determined by the permissible absolute value of the tensile stress in the turbine blades. Thus, for example, if it be assumed that for maximum values of the peripheral speed of the compressor $u_c = 450$ m/sec, the efficiency factor $\bar{G}_c = 0{\cdot}78$ and $\lambda_t = 0{\cdot}70$, then for a tensile stress of $\sigma_P = 2800$ kg/cm² the complex parameter will be equal to $u_c^2\bar{G}_c/\sigma_P q \cdot (\lambda_t) = 63{\cdot}1$, which, according to Fig. 28 corresponds to $T_H^* T_g^* = 0{\cdot}28$ and $\pi_c^* \geq 6{\cdot}0$. Therefore, for all values of $T_H^*/T_g^* > 0{\cdot}28$ it does not seem possible to assume simultaneously a peripheral speed of $u_c = 450$ m/sec and an efficiency factor of $\bar{G}_c = 0{\cdot}78$, if the indicated values of σ_P and λ_t are maintained. As a result of this, according to the extent of increase of T_H^*/T_g^*, it is necessary to reduce π_c^* for obtaining the maximum possible values of the complex parameter.

For example, for $M = 2{\cdot}5$, $H = 11$ km and the gas temperature $T_g^* = 1200$°K, the ratio $T_H^*/T_g^* = 0{\cdot}408$ and the maximum valu-

of the complex parameter for $\pi_c^*=4{\cdot}0$ will be equal to $\Pi=43$. Therefore, assuming that σ_p, u_c and λ_t remain uchanged, we obtain $\bar{G}_c=0{\cdot}53$. On the other hand, if for $M=2{\cdot}5$ it be assumed that $\bar{G}_c=0{\cdot}78$, then the permissible peripheral speed should amount to $u_c\approx 370$ m/sec.

Thus, the value of u_c permitted for maximum efficiency factor is obtained considerably lower than the peripheral speed arbitrarily assumed for the maximum value. It should be noted that $u_c=370$ m/sec and even lower peripheral speeds (340 – 350 m/sec) are used in a number of modern turbo-jet engines, and the maximum efficiency factors for them are $\bar{G}_{c.\max}=0{\cdot}65-0{\cdot}70$. Consequently, if such peripheral speeds are assumed also for high supersonic flight speeds ($M_H \geq 2{\cdot}5$), then the efficiency factor can attain a maximum value even for $\sigma_p < 2800$ kg/cm². However, the use of the maximum efficiency factor for $M_H \geq 2{\cdot}5$ in essence excludes the possibility of maintaining the r.p.m. at lower flight speeds. This is reflected adversely on the engine characteristics, since without special methods of control, it will be impossible to maintain the maximum gas temperature prior to the turbine in flight regimes at lower velocities. As a result, the take-off conditions, climb to altitude and other flight characteristics are impaired.

Further, if for $u_c=340-370$ m/sec a reduced value of the efficiency factor be assumed for an extension of the range of operation of the engine at a constant r.p.m., then in order to co-ordinate the operation of the compressor and the turbine it is necessary to reduce the tensile stress in the turbine blades. We shall suppose, for example, that for $M_H=2{\cdot}5$, $T_g^*=1200$°K and $\pi_c^*=4{\cdot}0$ it is accepted that: $u_c=350$ m/sec, $\lambda_t=0{\cdot}7$ and $\bar{G}_c=0{\cdot}53$, i.e. equal to $\bar{G}$ for $u_c=450$ m/sec. Since the value of $\Pi=43{\cdot}0$, then we obtain that $\sigma_p=1690$ kg/cm². Thus, a reduction in the peripheral speed in conjunction with the small value of $\bar{G}_c$ leads to a considerable reduction in σ_p. In such an engine it is necessary to have an increase in the number of stages of the turbine and of the compressor in comparison with an engine having a higher peripheral speed. However, in consequence of the reduction of stress of the turbine, the use of such an engine can, in a number of cases, have an adverse effect, if it is not substantially offset with respect to weight.

Some increase in the efficiency factor of the compressor and for a high peripheral speed may be achieved by means of increasing the gas temperature prior to the turbine, but for conditions of maintaining σ_P and simultaneously increasing π_c^*. Thus, for $T_g^* = 1500°K$ we obtain $T_H^*/T_g^* = 0{\cdot}326$ and in the case of an increase in π_c^* up to 6·0 we shall have $\Pi = 51$. This permits an efficiency factor of 0·663 (for $\sigma_P = 2800$ kg/cm², $\lambda_t = 0{\cdot}7$ and $u_c = 450$ m/sec) instead of 0·53, i.e. 20 per cent higher. However, there is a maximum efficiency factor, i.e. $\overline{G}_c = 0{\cdot}78$ for $M_H = 2{\cdot}5$ which is only possible for an extremely high gas temperature $T_g^* = 1740°K$, which corresponds to $T_H^*/T_g^* = 0{\cdot}28$.

In the case of an increase in σ_P by the use of more heat-resistant alloys or by the use of cooled blades, the efficiency factor may be raised, but for $G_{c.max}$ the stresses are required to be extremely high.

For example, for $M_H = 2{\cdot}5$ and $T_g^* = 1200°K$, in order to obtain $T^* = 1500°K$ then $\sigma_P = 3480$ kg/cm², which is difficult to realize even with cooled blades.

What has been stated shows that at high supersonic flight speeds one really must take into consideration either limiting the efficiency of the compressor or its peripheral speed.

It is important to point out that for selected values of σ_P and λ_t and consequently, for $u_c^2\overline{G}_c =$ const., a change of u_c and $\overline{G}_c$ within known limits exerts no practical influence on the weight of the engine. This is a consequence of the fact that for a small value of $\overline{G}_c$, but a higher peripheral speed, the diameter of the compressor increases, however at the same time the number of stages is decreased and consequently the weight of the compressor is slightly changed. All the remaining units of the engine (the turbine, combustion chamber, etc.) will, in both cases, be identical. Consequently, for a practically identical weight these engines will differ only in the diametrical dimensions and in the efficiency factor of the compressor.

For moderately supersonic and for subsonic flight speeds, the value of the complex parameter will usually be such that the peripheral speed and the efficiency factor of the compressor are not, as a rule, limited by the size of the turbine for conditions for which the expansion ratio is chosen sufficiently high (see Fig. 28).

In connection with this, in choosing the peripheral speed and efficiency factor for these conditions, it is essential primarily to proceed from the weight data, the characteristics of the engine and its reliability.

It should be noted that the compressor and the turbine of an engine intended for high values of M_H can be designed on a regime with small values of M_H for $\overline{G}_c = \overline{G}_{c.max}$ and for permissible values of σ_P.

Transition of this engine into the flight regime with high values of M_H and with a constant r.p.m. will take place for unchanged values of u_c, σ_P and λ_t, but with a reduction in $\overline{G}_c$ according to the extent of reduction of Π.

What has been discussed above can be extended also to turbo-jet engines with centrifugal or diagonal compressors, if one takes in these compressors for u_c the peripheral speed at the outside diameter of the inlet portion of the rotor, but the efficiency factor, just as in an axial compressor, is determined according to the value of λ_t and the relative diameter of the hub on entering the rotor.

It is important to note that in an engine with a centrifugal compressor having a single-sided inlet, even at high flight speeds (high values of T^*_H/T^*_g), the magnitude of $\overline{G}_c$ should be close to the maximum permissible or should exceed it, since the peripheral speed at the inlet diameter of the rotor is relatively small.

In order to reduce $\overline{G}_c$ it is necessary either to increase u_c, which for $\sigma_P = \text{const.}$ is associated with an increase in the overall size of the engine, or to use a supersonic inlet.

In an engine with a diagonal compressor, the value of u_c at the inlet diameter may be sufficiently small and consequently the efficiency factor for high supersonic flight velocities will be, just as for the presence of an axial compressor, relatively small.

Turbo-jet engine with a dual-cascade compressor. Equation (2.10) and the curves depicted in Fig. 28 are also applicable for choosing the peripheral speed and efficiency factor of a dual-cascade turbo-jet engine. For this one should take into account that the independence of the r.p.m. of the turbine, the rotary compressor of the first cascade (second turbine), from the r.p.m. of the first turbine permits higher stresses to be assigned to the turbine blades of the first cascade under certain conditions, since in two-stage turbines of turbo-jet engines the blades of the second stage frequently have a somewhat higher margin of continuous stability as a consequence of the limits imposed by the first stage.

In such cases, higher values of $\overline{G}_c$ in comparison with a single-cascade turbo-jet engine can be assumed for the required peripheral speed in the compressor of the first cascade, and its dimensions can be somewhat reduced in comparison with the dimensions of the first section of the compressor in a single-cascade turbo-jet engine.

It is necessary to point out at the same time that there is not always such a relationship in a two-stage turbine, and there may be the case when the second stage will be limiting with respect to stability safety, which is discussed below.

On the other hand, the compressor of the second cascade should be limited according to output to a greater extent than the compressor of the first cascade and the compressor of a single-cascade turbo-jet engine. This follows from the fact that for one and the same flight speed, the ratio T_H^*/T_g^* for the second cascade[1] is greater, as a consequence of the preheating of the air in the compressor of the first cascade. This is associated with a reduction in the complex parameter, in spite of the fact that the magnitude of Π for this cascade is determined by the expansion ratio in this cascade only, which, of course, is relatively small.

Moreover, σ_P in the turbine blades of the second cascade for identical material should be lower than in the turbine blades of the first cascade, in consequence of the higher gas temperature. Finally, in order to ensure a smooth air – gas flow over the entire turbine, the value of σ_t on discharge from the turbine of the second cascade will also be less than σ_t on discharge from the turbine of the first cascade.

A reduction of σ_P and λ_t at low values of Π involves a reduction in $\bar{G}_c$ also, since to reduce the peripheral speed correspondingly is not always expedient.

The reduced values of the efficiency factor in the compressor of the second cascade extend its possible operating range with respect to reduced output and reduced rotational speed. In spite of the reduced values of σ_P, the r.p.m. of the second cascade as a rule can be tolerated somewhat larger than the r.p.m. of the first cascade, which is explained by the relatively smaller area F_t in the turbine of the second cascade, in consequence of the increased density of the gas on discharge from this turbine.

In order to show this, we shall carry out a study for different values of π_c^* and T_H^*/T_g^*.

[1] By the quantity T_H in the given case is understood the overall temperature on entry into the compressor of the second cascade.

Resulting from conditions of stability and using equation (2.9), the relationship between the r.p.m. of the second and first cascades can be expressed in the following manner:

$$\frac{n_2}{n_1} = \sqrt{\left(\frac{\sigma_{p2} q(\lambda_t)_2 \sin \alpha_{t2}}{\sigma_{p1} q(\lambda_t)_1 \sin \alpha_{t1}} \pi_{t1}^{*(n_t+1)/2n_t}\right)}. \quad (2.16)$$

In this equation, the quantities with the index "1" refer to the compressor and turbine of the first cascade, and with the index "2" to the compressor and turbine of the second cascade.

By means of the parameters characterizing the efficiency and type of the turbines of both cascades, i.e. the turbine efficiency η_t^*, number of stages z and the quantity $Y^* = \sqrt{(\Sigma u^2/c^*_{\text{ad}})}$, the ratio of their r.p.m's can be further written down in the form

$$\frac{n_2}{n_1} = \frac{y_2}{y_1} \sqrt{\left(\frac{z_1}{z_2}\right)} \sqrt{\left[\frac{\eta_{t1}^*}{\eta_{t2}^*}\left(\frac{1}{L_{c1}/L_{c\Sigma}} - 1\right)\right]}, \quad (2.17)$$

where L_{c1} is the work expended on the compressor of the first cascade;

$L_{c\Sigma}$ is the work expended on the entire compressor.

Equation (2.17) is obtained on the assumption that the mean diameters of the turbines of the first and second cascades are identical.

Equating the right hand portions of equations (2.16) and (2.17) and denoting

$$c_1 = \frac{\sqrt{\left(\frac{\sigma_{p2} q(\lambda_t)_2 \sin \alpha_{t2}}{\sigma_{p1} q(\lambda_t)_2 \sin \alpha_{t1}}\right)}}{\frac{y_2^*}{y_1^*}\sqrt{\left(\frac{z_1}{z_2}\frac{\eta_{t1}^*}{\eta_{t2}^*}\right)}}$$

we obtain

$$\sqrt{\left(\frac{1}{L_{c1}/L_{c\Sigma}} - 1\right)} = c_1 \sqrt{\left(\pi_{t1}^{*(n_t+1)/2n_t}\right)}. \quad (2.18)$$

The ratio $L_{c1}/L_{c\Sigma}$ can be substituted by π_Σ and π_{t1}^* by means of the equation

$$\frac{L_{c1}}{L_{c\Sigma}} = \frac{1 - 1/\pi_{t1}^{*(k_g-1)/k_g}}{\left(\frac{\pi_{t\,\Sigma}^*}{\pi_{t1}^*}\right)^{(n_t-1)/n_t}\left(1 - 1/\pi_{t\,\Sigma}^{*(k_g-1)/k_g}\right)} \quad (2.19)$$

where

$$\pi^*_{t\Sigma} = \frac{1}{\left(1-\alpha\frac{T^*_H}{T^*_g}\frac{\pi^{*\,(k-1)/k}_{c\Sigma}-1}{\eta^*_c\,\eta^*_t}\right)^{(k_g-1)/k_g}}.$$

Substituting the value of $L_{c1}/L_{c\Sigma}$ from equation (2.19) in equation (2.18) we obtain

$$\pi^{*\,(n_t-1)/n_t}_{t\,\Sigma}(1-1/\pi^{*\,(k_g-1)/k_g}_{t\,2} =$$
$$= [c_1^2\pi^{*\,(n_t+1)/2n_t}_{t1}+1]\,(1-1/\pi^{*\,(k_g-1)/k_g}_{t1})\,\pi^{*\,(n_t-1)/n_t}_{t1}\,. \quad (2.20)$$

By means of this equation the value of π^*_{t1} can be determined for specified C_1 and $\pi^*_{t\Sigma}$ and the ratio between the r.p.m's n_2/n_1 can be found from equation (2.16).

Figure 30 shows the values of n_2/n_1 as a function of T^*_H/T^*_g for various values of $\pi^*_{c\Sigma}$.

It was assumed for the calculations that $z_1=z_2=1{\cdot}0$; $\eta^*_{t1}=\eta^*_{t2}$; $Y^*_1=Y^*_2$; $\sin\alpha_{t2}/\sin\alpha_{t1}=0{\cdot}97$; $n_t=1{\cdot}29$; $\eta^*_t=0{\cdot}91$ and $\eta^*_c=0{\cdot}83$.

For the ratios σ_{p2}/σ_{p1} and $q\,(\lambda_t)_2/q\,(\lambda_t)_1$ the mean values known from statistical data were used:

$$\sigma_{p2}/\sigma_{p1}=0{\cdot}725 \text{ and } q\,(\lambda_t)_2/q\,(\lambda_t)_1=0{\cdot}720.$$

Strictly speaking, the ratio σ_{p2}/σ_{p1} should be taken as dependent upon the distribution of the heat transfer through the stages and therefore the analysis with constant σ_{p2}/σ_{p1} is approximate.

It can be seen from Fig. 30 that for all parameters the ratio of the r.p.m's n_2/n_1 increases with increase of T^*_H/T^*_g, although the increase in T^*_H/T^*_g is connected with transition to high flight speeds, for which, as already mentioned, the first cascade is limited to a lesser degree by the efficiency of the compressor in relation to a single-cascade turbo-jet engine. Physically, this is a consequence of the fact that for one and the same $\pi^*_{c\,\Sigma}$ with increase of T^*_H/T^*_g the total expansion ratio is increased just as the expansion ratio in the turbine of the first cascade (π^*_{t1}). As a result of this, π^*_{t1} increases relatively more rapidly than does $\pi^*_{t\Sigma}$, and therefore the density of the gas on discharge from the turbine of the first cascade is reduced more rapidly than the density of the gas on discharge from the turbine of the second cascade, which is conditioned by the increase in the ratio n_2/n_1. It can be seen from equation (2.16) that the increase in π^*_{t1} for specified ratios of σ_{p2}/σ_{p1} and other values, leads to an increase in n_2/n_1.

It can also be seen from Fig. 30 that for small values of π_c^*, only slightly realistic for turbo-jet engines with a dual-cascade compressor, the r.p.m. of the second cascade are less than the r.p.m. of the first cascade for all values of T_H^*/T_g^*, which is explained by the small value of π_{t1}^*.

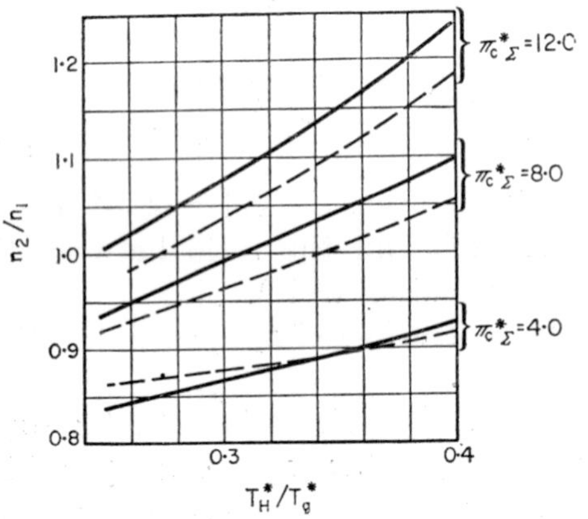

Fig. 30. Relationship between r.p.m. of the second and first cascades in a dual-cascade turbo-jet engine.

——— $\sigma_{p2}/\sigma_{p1} = 0{\cdot}725$;
— — — $\sigma_{p2}/\sigma_{p1} = f(\pi_{t1}^*, \pi_{t\Sigma}^*)$ for identical blade material for both turbines.

The relationship obtained between the r.p.m's of the second and first cascades can be made more precise by assuming that the ratio σ_{p2}/σ_{p1} is a function of the distribution of heat transfer between the cascade turbines. However, calculations show that such precision, in principle, does not alter the results obtained for constant values of σ_{p2}/σ_{p1}. For the example in Fig. 30 the change in n_2/n_1 is shown for the conditions such that

$$\frac{\sigma_{p2}}{\sigma_{p1}} = f(\pi_{t1}^*, \pi_{t\Sigma})$$

for identical material of the turbine blades of both cascades and for identical stability safety. The method of this calculation is similar to the method described below (pages 106–109).

Figure 31 shows the dependence of $L_{c1}/L_{c\Sigma}$ on T_H^*/T_g^* and $\pi_{c\Sigma}^*$ characterizing the distribution of the compression work between the separate cascades. The calculations were carried out according to equation (2.19).

From the equation for the equality of the air flow rates through the intake sections of the compressors of the first and second cascades we obtain

$$\frac{n_2}{n_1} = \frac{u_{c2}}{u_{c1}} \sqrt{\left(\frac{\bar{G}_{c2}}{\bar{G}_{c1}} \pi_{c1}^{*\,(n_c+1)/2n_c}\right)}$$

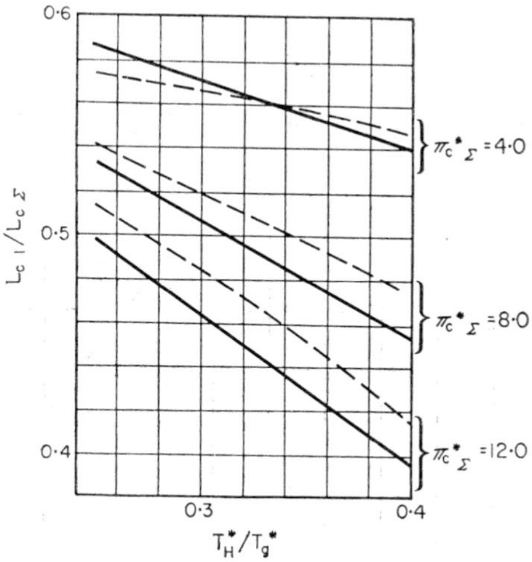

Fig. 31. Relative magnitude of the compression work in the compressor of the first cascade.
———— $\sigma_{p2}/\sigma_{p1} = 0{\cdot}725$;
— — — $\sigma_{p2}/\sigma_{p1} = f\,(\pi_{t1}^*,\ \pi_{t\Sigma}^*)$ for identical blade material for both cascade turbines.

where G_{c1} and G_{c2} are the efficiency factors of the compressor of the first and second cascades;

π_{c1}^* is the expansion ratio in the compressor of the first cascade;

n_c is the index for the polytropic process of compression in the compressor of the first cascade;

u_{c1} and u_{c2} are the peripheral speeds of the first stages of the compressors of the first and second cascades.

From the previous equation we have

$$\frac{\bar{G}_{c2}}{\bar{G}_{c1}} = \frac{(n_2/n_1)^2\,(u_{c1}/u_{c2})^2}{\pi_c^{*(n_c+1)/2n_c}} \tag{2.21}$$

where

$$\pi^*_{c1} = \left[\frac{L_{c1}}{L_{c\Sigma}}\,\frac{\eta^*_{c1}}{\eta^*_{c\Sigma}}\left(\pi^{*\,(k-1)/k}_{c\Sigma} - 1\right) + 1\right]^{k/(k-1)}.$$

Using the data from the previous calculations, by determining n_2/n_1 and $L_{c1}/L_{c\Sigma}$ we obtain the possibility of calculating the ratio $\bar{G}_{c2}/\bar{G}_{c1}$ as a function of T^*_H/T^*_g and π^*_c for different values of u_{c1}/u_{c2}. Figure 32 shows the variation of $\bar{G}_{c2}/\bar{G}_{c1}$ for identical peripheral speeds and for this condition we have $\bar{G}_{c2}/\bar{G}_{c1} < 1{\cdot}0$.

If, for one and the same n_2/n_1 the peripheral speed be reduced of the compressor of the second cascade, i.e., if we take $u_{c1}/u_{c2} > 1{\cdot}0$,

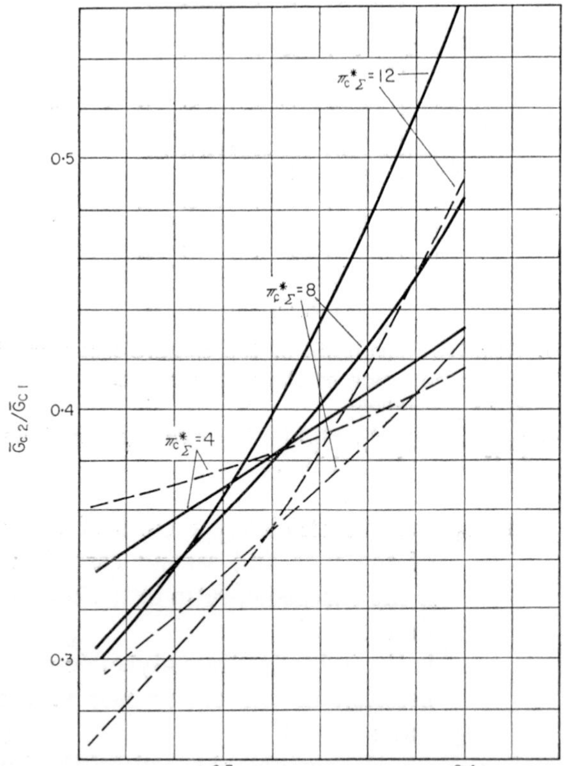

Fig. 32. Relationship between the efficiency factors of the first and second cascade compressors.
$\sigma_{p2}/\sigma_{p1} = 0{\cdot}725$;
$\sigma_{p2}/\sigma_{p1} = f\,(\pi^*_{t1}, \pi^*_{t\Sigma})$ for identical blade material for both cascade turbines.

then the ratio $\bar{G}_{c2}/\bar{G}_{c1}$ can be increased. However, for $n_2/n_1 > 1{\cdot}0$, this is associated with a further decrease in the diameter of the compressor of the second cascade relative to the first, which is not always structurally possible. Moreover, as a result of this, it is necessary to increase the number of stages of the compressor of the second cascade. Therefore, as a rule, $\bar{G}_{c2}/\bar{G}_{c1}$ should be less than unity and, consequently, the conclusions made earlier on the basis of the analysis of the complex parameter Π are verified.

Dual-circuit turbo-jet engines. For a dual-circuit engine, the complex parameter is expressed by the equation

$$\frac{u_c^2\bar{G}_c}{\sigma_p q(\lambda_t)} =$$

$$= \frac{1}{1-\beta}\,\frac{\sin\alpha_t\delta_t\pi_c^*\sqrt{\left(\frac{T_H^*}{T_g^*}\right)}\left[1-a\frac{T_H^*}{T_g^*}\frac{\pi_c^{*(k-1)/k}-1}{\eta_c^*\eta_t^*}\left(1+\frac{\beta}{1-\beta}\frac{L_{c2}}{L_{c1}}\right)\right]^{k_g/(k_g-1)}}{0{\cdot}0439\nu_t\Phi\sqrt{\left[1-a\frac{T_H^*}{T_g^*}\frac{\pi_c^{*(k-1)/k}-1}{\eta_c^*}\left(1+\frac{\beta}{1-\beta}\frac{L_{c2}}{L_c}\right)\right]}} \tag{2.22}$$

where $\beta = G_{a2}/G_a$ is the ratio of the air flow rate through the second circuit to the overall air flow rate through the engine;

L_{c2} is the work expended on the compressor of the second circuit;

L_{c1} is the work expended on the compressor of the first circuit.

In order to obtain the possibility of carrying out a generalized study of the complex parameter in a dual-circuit turbo-jet engine, we shall write its ratio to the complex parameter for a turbo-jet engine, by assuming that the parameters

$$\lambda_t,\ \alpha_t,\ \delta_t,\ \pi_c^*,\ T_H^*/T_g^* \text{ and } \nu_t$$

are identical in both cases.

Denoting this ratio by Π, we obtain

$$\pi = \frac{1}{1-\beta}\,\frac{\left[1-a\frac{T_H^*}{T_g^*}\frac{l(\pi_c^*)}{\eta_t^*}\left(1+\frac{\beta}{1-\beta}\frac{L_{c2}}{L_{c1}}\right)^{k_g/(k_g-1)}\right]\sqrt{\left(1-a\frac{T_H^*}{T_g^*}\frac{l(\pi_c^*)}{\eta_t^*}\right)}}{\sqrt{\left[1-a\frac{T_H^*}{T_g^*}\,l(\pi_c^*)\left(1+\frac{\beta}{1-\beta}\frac{L_{c2}}{L_c}\right)\right]}\left[1-a\frac{T_H^*}{T_g^*}\frac{l(\pi_c^*)}{\eta_t^*}\right]^{k_g/k_g-1}} \tag{2.23}$$

For $\eta_t^* = \text{const.}$ and $a = \text{const.}$, the quantity $\varPi$ can be considered as a function of three quantities

$$\pi = f\left[\frac{T_H^*}{T_g^*}\, l(\pi_c^*)\,;\ \beta\,;\ \frac{L_{c2}}{L_{c1}}\right],$$

where

$$\frac{T_H^*}{T_g^*}\, l(\pi_c^*) = \frac{L_c}{\dfrac{k}{k-1} R T_g^*}.$$

This analysis of the value of $\varPi$ permits a general law to be developed for its variation as a function of β and L_{c2}/L_{c1}, and also as a function of the speed and altitude of flight, gas temperature and expansion ratio.

Figure 33 shows the dependence of $\varPi$ on the product $(T_H^*/T_g^*)(\pi_c^*)$ for certain values of β and L_{c2}/L_{c1}. It can be seen from Fig. 33

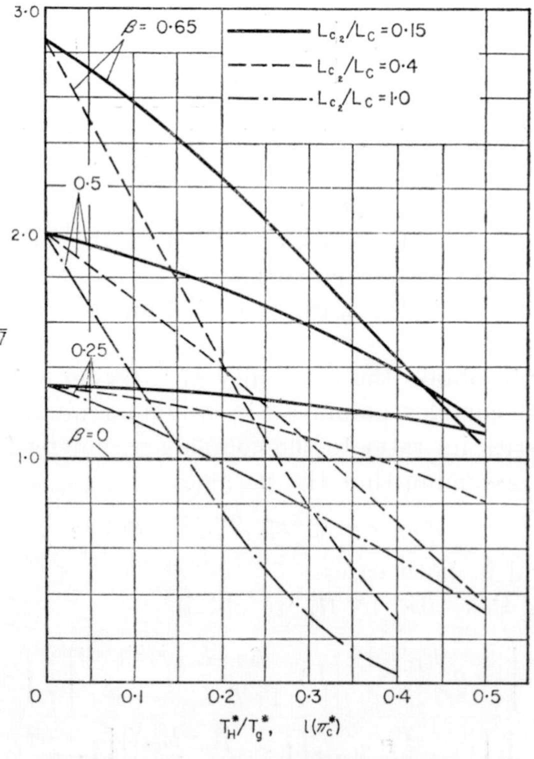

Fig. 33. Relative variation of the complex parameter for dual-circuit engines.

that for all values of $\beta > 0$ the value of Π is reduced according to the extent of increase of $(T_H^*/T_g^*)\ l\ (\pi_c^*)$.

Consequently, with increase of flight speed (increase of T_H^*) for a given gas temperature and expansion ratio, the complex parameter for a dual-circuit turbo-jet engine is reduced, since under these conditions it is also reduced in turbo-jet engines (see Fig. 28).

Conversely, an increase in the gas temperature for a given value of T_H^* (i.e. in speed and flight altitude) and of π_c^* increases both Π and the absolute value of the complex parameter in a dual-circuit turbo-jet engine.

An increase in the expansion ratio for a given value of T_H^*/T_g^* gives rise to a reduction of Π, whereupon the absolute value of the complex parameter will be a maximum for certain values of π_c^*, associated with the fact that there is a maximum for the complex parameter also in turbo-jet engines.

For a value of $L_{c2}/L_{c1} = 0{\cdot}15$, values of $\Pi > 1{\cdot}0$ for all values of β and $(T_H^*/T_g^*)\ l\ (\pi_c^*)$ are presented in Fig. 33. If the data of the example discussed above be used, i.e. $M = 2{\cdot}5$; $T_H^*/T_g^* = 0{\cdot}425$ and $\pi_c^* = 4{\cdot}0$, then the product $(T_H^*/T_g^*)\ l\ (\pi_c^*) = 0{\cdot}25$ (for $\eta_c^* = 0{\cdot}83$). Hence we obtain the following values for Π as a function of β for $L_{c2}/L_{c1} = 0{\cdot}15$:

β	0·25	0·5	0·65
Π	1·25	1·66	2·05

For identical peripheral speeds in the compressors of a turbo-jet engine and in a dual-circuit turbo-jet engine, identical stresses in the blades of the last stage of the turbine and values of λ_t, the efficiency factor for the compressor of a dual-circuit turbo-jet engine increases to the same extent as does the value of Π.

In particular, for $\beta = 0{\cdot}5$ the efficiency factor of the compressor of a dual-circuit turbo-jet engine should amount to $\sim 0{\cdot}795$ as against 0·478 in the compressor of a turbo-jet engine. This value is, in practice, limiting with respect to its magnitude. For $\beta = 0{\cdot}65$ the limiting value of $\bar{G}_c$ can be obtained for a lower stress in the turbine blades, or a lower λ_t, than in a turbo-jet engine, i. e. the turbine in the case mentioned will not limit the choice of the output and peripheral speed of the compressor.

Thus, for small values of L_{c2}/L_{c1} and sufficiently large values of Π, the peripheral speed and the efficiency factor of the compressor of the first circuit in a dual-circuit turbo-jet engine even at high supersonic flight velocities can be assumed to be limitingly large with respect to magnitude.

With increase of L_{c2}/L_{c1}, i.e. the ratio of the work in the compressors of the first and second circuit, a reduction of Π according to the extent of increase of T^*_H/T^*_g and of $l(\pi^*_c)$ takes place more rapidly, as a result of which the value of Π may be less than unity and, consequently a dual-circuit turbo-jet engine will give way to a single-circuit engine according to the compressor output for identical peripheral speeds of the compressor and identical stresses in the turbine blades and $q(\lambda_t)$.

Thus, for example, for $\beta = 0{\cdot}5$ and $L_{c2}/L_{c1} = 0{\cdot}4$ the value of $\Pi < 1{\cdot}0$ for $(T^*_H/T^*_g)\ l(\pi^*_c) > 0{\cdot}32$. Therefore, if $T^*_H/T^*_g = 0{\cdot}425$ and $\eta^*_c = 0{\cdot}83$, then for $\pi^*_c > 5{\cdot}5$ the value of $\Pi < 1{\cdot}0$. For $\beta = 0{\cdot}25$ and $L_{c2}/L_{c1} = 1{\cdot}0$, the value of $\Pi < 1{\cdot}0$, if for $T^*_H/T^*_g = 0{\cdot}425$ the value of $\pi^*_c > 3{\cdot}0$ and if for $T^*_H/T^*_g = 0{\cdot}363$ the value of $\pi^*_c > 3{\cdot}5$.

It is necessary to point out that for every value of L_{c2}/L_{c1} there is a certain limiting value of β, and conversely for every value of β there is a limiting value of L_{c2}/L_{c1} which is physically determined by the condition when the expansion in the turbine takes place at atmospheric pressure.

Thus, the pressure drop in the turbine for this limiting case can be written in the following form:

$$\pi^*_{t.\mathrm{lim}} = \frac{p^*_g}{p_H}\,\Pi(\lambda_t) = \frac{p^*_c\delta_g}{p_H}\,\Pi(\lambda_t)\,,$$

where

$$\Pi(\lambda_t) = \left(1 - \frac{k_g - 1}{k_g + 1}\,\lambda_t^2\right)^{k_g/(k_g-1)}.$$

On the other hand

$$p_H = p^*_H\,\Pi(\lambda_H) = \frac{p^*_a}{\delta_i}\,\Pi(\lambda_H)\,.$$

Substituting the value of p_H and $p^*_c/p^*_a = \pi^*_c$, we obtain

$$\pi^*_{t.\mathrm{lim}} = \pi^*_c\delta_g\delta_i\frac{\Pi(\lambda_t)}{\Pi(\lambda_H)}\,. \tag{2.24}$$

An increase in π_c^* or in the flight speed λ_H leads to an increase in $\pi_{t.\text{lim}}$.

From the equation of work balance of the turbine and compressor of the first and second circuits we obtain

$$m\frac{L_{c2}}{L_{c1}}=\frac{\left(1-\frac{1}{\pi_t^{*(kg-1)/kg}}\right)\eta_t^*}{a\frac{T_H^*}{T_g^*}\,l(\pi_c^*)}-1 \tag{2.25}$$

where $m=G_{a2}/G_{a1}$ is the ratio of the air flow rate through the second circuit to the air flow rate through the first circuit.

The quantities m and β are connected by the relationship

$$m=\frac{\beta}{1-\beta}.$$

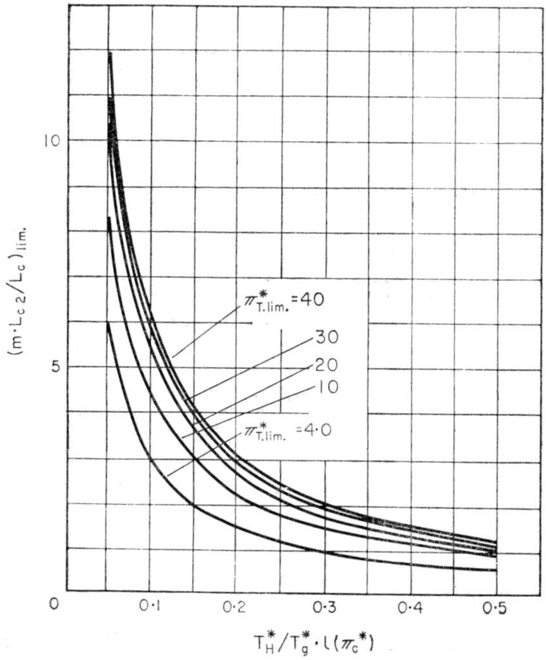

Fig. 34. Limiting values of the quantity $m\frac{L_{c2}}{L_{c1}}$ for a dual-circuit turbo-jet engine.

If $\pi_t^* = \pi_{t.\text{lim}}$, then the product $m\,(L_{c2}/L_{c1})$ in equation (2.24) wil have a limiting value and, consequently, the choice of one co-factor will predetermine also the value of the second one.

Figure 34 shows the variation of $m\,(L_{c2}/L_{c1})$ as a function of $(T_H^*/T_g^*)\,l\,(\pi_c^*)$ for a number of finite values of π_t^*.

Knowing the value of T_H^*/T_g^* and π_c^*, it is easy to find by means of the graph the limiting value of $m\,(L_{c2}/L_{c1})$ if formula (2.24) is used for calculating $\pi_{t.\text{lim}}^*$.

In the special case of an engine with air separation after the compressor, when $L_{c2}/L_{c1} = 1{\cdot}0$, we obtain from the curves presented in Fig. 34. the limiting values of m and, consequently, β.

The analysis described is just as applicable to a single-shaft as to a dual-shaft dual-circuit turbo-jet engine. However, in the latter there is a possibility of choosing a higher r.p.m. for the first circuit since in a single-shaft dual-circuit turbo-jet engine the r.p.m., as follows from what has been stated above, will be determined primarily not by the limiting power of the turbine, but by the compressor of the second circuit, the diameter of which is considerably larger than the diameter of the first circuit. As a result of this, the peripheral speeds of the compressor of the first circuit and of the turbine are reduced. The possibility of increasing these peripheral speeds in a twin-shaft design permits the number of stages of the compressor and of the turbine to be reduced.

Turbo-prop engines. For a single shaft turbo-prop engine, the general expression for the complex parameter can be written in the same form as for a turbo-jet engine:

$$\frac{u_c^2 G_c}{\sigma_p q(\lambda_t)} = \frac{\sin \alpha_t \sigma_g \pi_c^* \sqrt{(T_H^*)}}{0{\cdot}0439 \nu_g \Phi \sqrt{(T_t^*)} \pi_t^*}.$$

If we express the overall expansion ratio in the turbine π_t^* in the following manner:

$$\pi_t^* = \pi_{t.c}^* \pi_{t.p}^*$$

where $\pi_{t.c}^*$ is the pressure differential required for rotating the compressor;

$\pi_{t.p}^*$ is the pressure differential expended on the propellor and on the nozzle, then we can write

$$T_t^* = \frac{T_{t.k}^*}{\pi_{t.p}^{*\,(n_t-1)/n_t}}$$

where n_t is the polytropic expansion index in the turbine.

As a result we obtain

$$\Pi_{\text{turbo-prop}} = \Pi_{\text{turbo-jet}} \frac{\sqrt{\left(\pi_{t.p}^{*\,(n_t-1)/n_t}\right)}}{\pi_{t.p}^*} = \frac{\Pi_{\text{turbo-jet}}}{\pi_{t.p}^{*\,(n_t+1)/2n_t}} .$$

In order to calculate $\pi_{t.p}^*$ it is easy to obtain a simple formula by using the following derivation:

$$\pi_{t.p}^* = \frac{p_{t.c}^*}{p_t^*} = \frac{p_{t.c}^* \Pi(\lambda_t)}{\varepsilon p_H} ,$$

where $\varepsilon \geq 1{\cdot}0$ is the coefficient of increase of static pressure behind the turbine relative to atmospheric pressure.

Moreover, we can write

$$p_H = p_H^* \Pi(\lambda_H) = \frac{p_a^*}{\sigma_i} \Pi(\lambda_H) ,$$

where λ_H is the flight velocity coefficient.

Further

$$p_{t.c}^* = \frac{p_g^*}{\pi_{t.c}^*} = \frac{p_c^* \delta_g}{\pi_{t.c}^*} ,$$

therefore

$$\pi_{t.p}^* = \frac{p_c^* \delta_g \Pi(\lambda_t) \delta_{in}}{\varepsilon p_a^* \Pi(\lambda_H) \pi_{t.c}^*} = \frac{\pi_c^* \delta_g \delta_{in} \Pi(\lambda_g)}{\varepsilon \Pi(\lambda_H) \pi_{t.c}^*} .$$

Substituting $\pi_{t.p}^*$ by the expression from the work balance equation, we have

$$\pi_{t.p}^* = \frac{\pi_k^* \delta_g \delta_{in} \Pi(\lambda_t)}{\varepsilon \Pi(\lambda_H)} \left(1 - a \frac{T_H^*}{T_g^*} \, \frac{\pi_c^{*(k-1)/k} - 1}{\eta_c^* \eta_g^*}\right)^{k/(k-1)} .$$

Since $\pi_{t.p}^* \gg 1{\cdot}0$, then consequently the complex parameter for a turbo-prop engine will always be substantially less than the complex parameter for a turbo-jet engine, and therefore in a turbo-prop engine limitations with respect to peripheral speed or output will always be quite appreciable.

Let us take an example: $\pi_c^* = 6{\cdot}0$, $\sigma_g = 0{\cdot}97$, $\sigma_{in} = 0{\cdot}98$, $\lambda_t = 0{\cdot}7$, $\Pi(\lambda_t) = 0{\cdot}7483$, $\lambda_H = 0{\cdot}826$, $\Pi(\lambda_H) = 0{\cdot}655$, $\frac{T^*_{II}}{T^*_g} = \frac{244}{1200} = 0{\cdot}203$.

For these conditions $\Pi_{\text{turbo-jet}} = 63$, $\pi^*_{t.p} = 2{\cdot}72$ and consequently

$$\Pi_{\text{turbo-prop}} = \frac{63}{2{\cdot}72^{0{\cdot}89}} = 25{\cdot}8.$$

If we assume that $\sigma_p = 2500$ kg/cm², $u_c = 350$ m/sec, then we obtain, for a turbo-prop engine $\overline{G}_c = 0{\cdot}471$.

Thus, in a single-shaft turbo-prop engine, even for a moderate peripheral speed the efficiency factor of the compressor should be extremely small.

In a twin-shaft turbo-prop engine, the turbine turning the compressor will not, in practice, limit the choice of the peripheral speed and the output of the compressor associated with small values of T^*_H/T^*_g at subsonic flight velocities and high values of π^*_c.

Summarizing the situation, it can be stated that the method discussed for linking the engine parameters and the flight conditions with the primary aerodynamic and design data of the compressor and turbine by means of the complex parameter, or the criterion of comparison Π, is of a general nature and permits the rational parameters to be investigated for engines of a different type.

The Relationship Connecting Engine Parameters and Flight Conditions with the Output and Type of Turbine

In the analysis recounted above, the turbine was characterized by the quantities σ_p and λ_t, but for the remaining data (α_t, Φ), entering into equation (2.10), constants were assumed.

For variable values of α_t and Φ the complex parameter will vary proportionally with the value of $\sin \alpha_t$ (Φ) i.e. it is increased with increase of the angle α_t and with decrease of the shape factor Φ, assuming the law of variation of the cross-sections of the blade with respect to height.

The angle α_t of the gas stream on exit from the turbine usually differs but little from 90°, and therefore $\sin \alpha$ can vary within extremely narrow limits.

The value of $\Phi = 0{\cdot}5$, assumed in the calculations (see Fig. 28), corresponds to the modern level of this coefficient, but looking ahead it should become somewhat further reduced, which will permit an increase in the complex parameter.

A further increase in the shape factor Φ will lead to a reduction of the complex parameter, and consequently to a reduction in output or in the peripheral speed of the compressor. Moreover, as a result of this the weight of the blades and of the turbine disc will be increased, and therefore such a course is ruled out.

Let us consider the relationship between the engine parameters and certain turbine data. In particular, in order to assess the overall size of the turbocompressor part of the engine it is important to consider the ratio of the turbine diameter to that of the compressor and the dependence of this ratio upon the number of stages and other quantities.

We shall introduce for the last stage of the turbine the concept of efficiency factor, analogous with the efficiency factor of the compressor. For an angle of discharge of the flow of $\alpha_t \neq 90°$ we obtain

$$\bar{G}_t = \frac{G_{g.t}}{G_{g.to}} = q(\lambda_t)\,(1-\bar{d}_t^2)\sin\alpha_t\,, \tag{2.26}$$

where $\bar{d}_t$ is the relative diameter of the hub of the last stage.

The tensile stress in the blades can be linked with $\bar{G}_t$.

With the aid of equations (2.4) and (2.5) we obtain

$$\sigma_p = 0{\cdot}0439\, u_t^2\,(1-\bar{d}_t^2)\,\Phi. \tag{2.27}$$

Multiplying and dividing the right hand portion of this equation by $q\,(\lambda_t)\sin\,\alpha_t$ we have

$$\sigma_p = 0{\cdot}0439\frac{u_t^2\bar{G}_t}{q(\lambda_t)\sin\alpha_t}\,. \tag{2.28}$$

Substituting this expression for σ_p in equation (2.10) and denoting the ratio of the peripheral speed of the turbine to the peripheral speed of the compressor by $\bar{u} = u_t/u_c$, we can write down the following equation

$$\frac{\bar{G}_c}{\bar{u}^2\bar{G}_t} = \frac{0{\cdot}0439\Phi}{\sin\alpha_t}\;\frac{u_c^2\bar{G}_c}{\sigma_p q(\lambda_t)} = \frac{0{\cdot}0439\Phi}{\sin\alpha_t}\,\Pi\,. \tag{2.29}$$

Since $u_t/u_c = D_t/D_c$, then in place of $\bar{u}$ it can be taken that $\bar{D} = D_t/D_c$ and therefore the quantity $\bar{G}_c/\bar{u}^2\bar{G}_t$ is written in the form $\bar{G}_c/\bar{D}^2\bar{G}_t$.

For constant values of Φ and α_t the quantity $\bar{G}_c/\bar{D}^2\bar{G}_t$ is proportional to the complex parameter $\Pi = u_c^2\bar{G}_c/\sigma_p\ q\ (\lambda_t)$ and, consequently the regularity of the variation of this value from T_H^*/T_g^* and π_c^* should be the same as the regularity of variation of the complex parameter. In particular, it is obvious that if we assume the efficiency factors of the turbine and compressor to be constants, then with increase of T_H^*/T_g^* the ratio $\bar{D} = D_t/D_c$ should be increased, since a reduction in the complex parameter will occur and, consequently in the quantity $\bar{G}_c/\bar{D}^2\bar{G}_t$. If further it be assumed that $\bar{G}_t$=const. and $\bar{D}$ = const., then the efficiency factor of the compressor will be reduced. In the case of an increase in $\bar{D}$ for specified values of T_H^*/T_g^* and π_c^*, the efficiency factor of the compressor also increases, whereupon if $\bar{G}_t$=const. this will be associated with a reduction in the diameter of the compressor, since the diameter of the turbine will remain unchanged.

This follows from the fact that

$$D_t^2 = \frac{G_g\sqrt{(T_t^*)}}{\pi S p_t^* \bar{G}_t}.$$

For specified values of G_g, T_H^*, T_g^* and π_c^* we obtain

$$D_t^2 = \text{const.}/\bar{G}_t \quad \text{or} \quad \bar{G}_t D_t^2 = \text{const.}$$

Consequently, for $\bar{G}_t$=constant, D_t should also be constant.

An increase in the efficiency factor of the compressor for large values of T_H^*/T_g^* can also be attained for D_t/D_c=const., but by means of increasing the efficiency factor of the turbine, which depends upon λ_t and $\bar{d}_t$. In this case the diameters of both the turbine and the compressor will also be reduced. Actually, since for specified values of T_H^*, T_g^* and π_c^*, $\bar{G}_t D_t^2$=const., then for an increase in $\bar{G}$ here will be a reduction in D_t, and for D_t/D_c=const. the value of D_c should also be reduced.

For single-stage turbines of turbo-jet engines with centrifugal compressors, the following data are characteristic: λ_t=0·65 – 0·7; $\bar{d}_t$=0·7 – 0·72 and $\bar{G}_t$=0·43 – 0·46. For the second stages of two-stage turbines average data are λ_t=0·6 – 0·7; $\bar{d}_t$=0·6 – 0·7 and $\bar{G}_t$=0·42 – 0·57.

An increase in λ_t above 0·7 will strongly limit the operating regime of the turbine and will give rise to an increase in the losses in the jet pipe. Therefore, such an increase in λ_t is possible only in isolated cases. An increase in the efficiency factor of the turbine

$\overline{G}_t$ (for and increase in $\overline{G}_c$), at the expense of a reduction in the relative diameter of the hub of the last stage, is also possible within close limits, since it should be assumed that $\overline{d}_{t.\min} \approx 0{\cdot}45 - 0{\cdot}5$.

For a reduction in $\overline{d}_t$ it is necessary to either increase the stress in the turbine blades or to reduce u_t for $\sigma_p = \text{const.}$ (see equation 2.27). The latter is connected with a reduction in u/C^*_{ad} or with an increase in the number of stages.

If, for large values of T^*_H/T^*_g a small efficiency factor be used in the compressor for extending the operating range of the engine for $n = \text{const.}$, then, consequently, reduced values of D_t/D_c, u_t/u_c and $\overline{G}_t$ should be used. For this the diameter and peripheral speed of the compressor should be increased, but if the magnitude of the peripheral speed of the compressor is limited to a relatively small value, then a reduction in D_t/D_c and in u_t/u_c is associated with a reduction of the r.p.m and peripheral speed of the turbine and with the necessity of increasing the number of stages.

However, in contrast to the case when $\overline{G}_c$ was large in value, the stress in the turbine blades should be reduced, which was shown above.

The relationship between the diameter of the turbine and the compressor can be further represented in a form independent of $\overline{G}_t$ and also of λ_t and $\overline{d}_t$, and which will enable the effect of the various factors to be more clearly shown.

With the aid of equation (2.28) we obtain

$$\frac{D_c}{D_t} = \xi_0 \sqrt{\left(\Pi \frac{\overline{G}_t}{\overline{G}_c}\right)},$$

where

$$\xi_0 = \frac{0{\cdot}0439\Phi}{\sin \alpha_t}.$$

Solving for the values of Π and $\overline{G}_t$, this equation can be further given in the following form:

$$\frac{D_c}{D_t} = \xi_0 \sqrt{\left(\frac{u_c^2}{\sigma_p}(1-\overline{d}_t^2)\right)}. \tag{2.30}$$

We shall substitute the value of $(1-d_t^2)$ by means of the following transformation. If it be assumed that the mean diameters of the turbine stages are identical, then we can write

$$Y^* = \frac{u_{\text{av}}\sqrt{z}}{c^*_{\text{ad}}}.$$

Substituting u_{av} by u_t and $\bar{d}_t$, we obtain

$$Y^* = \frac{u_t(1+\bar{d}_t)\sqrt{z}}{2c^*_{ad}}.$$

By means of this equation we find

$$1-\bar{d}_t^2 = 1-\left(\frac{2Y^*c^*_{ad}}{u_t\sqrt{z}}-1\right)^2.$$

On the other hand from equations (2.4) and (2.5) we obtain

$$1-\bar{d}_t^2 = \frac{2g\sigma_p}{\gamma_b u_t^2 \Phi}.$$

Equating the right hand sides of the last two equations, we find

$$u_t = \frac{\sqrt{z}}{4Y^*c^*_{ad}}\left[\frac{2g\sigma_p}{\gamma_b\Phi}+\frac{4Y^{*2}c^{*2}_{ad}}{z}\right]^2.$$

Using the expression for u_t so obtained, we get

$$1-\bar{d}_t^2 = \frac{2g\sigma_p}{\gamma_b\Phi\left[\frac{\sqrt{z}}{4Y^*c^*_{ab}}\left(\frac{2g\sigma_p}{\gamma_b\Phi}+\frac{4Y^{*2}c^{*2}_{ad}}{z}\right)\right]^2}.$$

Therefore the ratio D_c/D_t can be represented in the form

$$\frac{D_c}{D_t} = \frac{\xi_1\sqrt{u_c^2/\sigma_p}}{(\xi_2/X)+X} \tag{2.31}$$

where

$$\xi_1 = 10^2\sqrt{\left(\frac{0{\cdot}0439\times 2g}{\sin\alpha_t\gamma_b}\right)};$$

$$\xi_2 = 10^4\frac{2g}{4\gamma_b\Phi};$$

$$X = \frac{Y^*c^*_{ad}}{\sqrt{z}\sqrt{\sigma_p}} = \frac{Y^*\sqrt{(2gL^*_{adt})}}{\sqrt{z}\sqrt{\sigma_p}}.$$

The dimensions of g, u_c, γ_b are expressed in m/sec²; m/sec and kg/m³, respectively, and the dimension σ_p is assumed to be in kg/cm². This is assumed by the value of the coefficients ξ_1 and ξ_2.

Equation (2.31) gives a generalized relationship for D_c/D_t. Figure 35 shows the dependence of D_c/D_t on X for various values of u_c^2/σ_p.

In the calculations values are assumed of $\Phi = 0{\cdot}5$, $\sin \alpha_t = 0{\cdot}995$, $\gamma_b = 8{\cdot}4 \,.\, 10^3$ kg/m³.

For $X = \sqrt{\xi_2}$ the ratio D_c/D_t has a maximum value for all values of u_c^2/σ_P. With an increase in X beyond $X = \sqrt{\xi_2}$ independently of how this increase occurs the ratio D_c/D_t decreases. Thus, for an increase in Y^* or c_{ad}^* or for a reduction in the number of stages and σ_P, the diameter of the turbine increases and the ratio D_c/D_t is reduced.

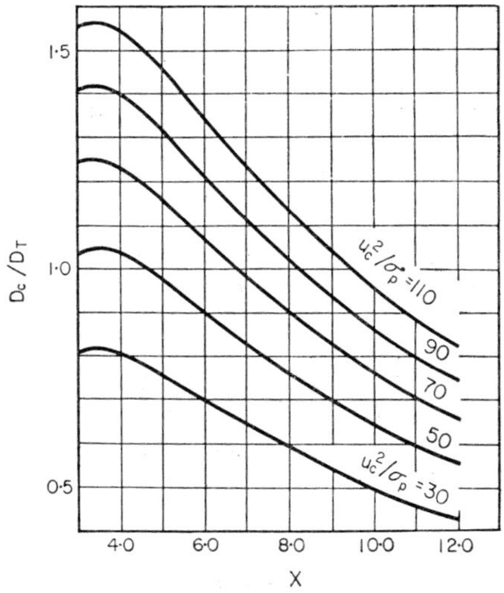

Fig. 35. Dependence of D_c/D_t on X.

It can be seen from equation (2.31) and Fig. 35 that the ratio D_c/D_t depends further to a strong degree on the quantity u_c^2/σ_P. Since the latter quantity enters into the complex parameter $\Pi = u_c^2 \overline{G}_c / \sigma_P \, q \, (\lambda_t)$, then its value, and equally so D_c/D_t for every expansion ratio, and the ratio T_H^*/T_g^* will be determined by the numerical value of the complex parameter and by selected values of $\overline{G}_c$ and $q\,(\lambda_t)$.

This relationship is partially discussed above, and is also used in the following chapter for investigating the effect of the expansion ratio and of the gas temperature on the sizes of the compressor and turbine.

In conclusion we shall discuss further the problem concerning the relationship between the tensile stresses and the safety factor in the blades of the first and second stages of the turbine, which is of considerable value, since the stress in the last stage of the turbine enters into the complex parameter and, consequently, it is indeed this stress which is decisive.

On the basis of equation (2.8) the relationship between the tensile stresses is written down in the form

$$\frac{\sigma_{p1}}{\sigma_{p2}} = \frac{q\lambda_{t2}}{q\lambda_{t1}} \frac{\sin\alpha_{t2}}{\sin\alpha_{t1}} \frac{1}{\pi_{t_2}^{*\,(n_t+1)/2n_t}},$$

where the quantity with the index "1" corresponds to the first stage of the turbine and the index "2" corresponds to the second stage of the turbine.

If the pressure drop in the first stage $\pi_{t_1}^*$ is expressed by $\pi_{t\Sigma}^*$ in the form

$$\pi_{t_1}^* = \psi\pi_{t\Sigma}^*,$$

then the pressure drop in the second stage will be $\pi_{t_2}^* = 1/\psi$.

The quantity ψ is obtained by the equation

$$\psi = \left[\frac{1 - \dfrac{L_{\mathrm{ad}\cdot t}^*}{k_g/(k_g-1)RT_g^*}}{1 - \dfrac{\mu L_{\mathrm{ad}\cdot t\Sigma}^*}{k_g/(k_g-1)RT_g^*}}\right]^{k_g/(k_g-1)}$$

where

$$\mu = \frac{L_{\mathrm{ad}\cdot t1}^*}{L_{\mathrm{ad}\cdot t}^*}.$$

The coefficient μ characterizes the distribution of the heat transfer between the stages of the turbine. The velocity coefficient λ_t and the angle α_t on discharge from the second stage of the turbine is greater than for the first stage of the turbine.

As an average value one can assume

$$\frac{q(\lambda_t)_2 \sin\alpha_{t2}}{q(\lambda_t)_1 \sin\alpha_{t1}} = 1{\cdot}5.$$

Figure 36 shows the dependence of σ_{p1}/σ_{p2} on T_H^*/T_g^* for various values of π_c^* and μ. It can be seen from the curves that for an increase of T_H^*/T_g^* and π_c^* the level of the stress in the blades of the first turbine is reduced in comparison with that of the second. Consequently, for high supersonic flight velocities, characterizing increases in the values of T_H^*/T_g^* and also for high π_c^*, the tensile stresses in the blades of the second stage will be higher.

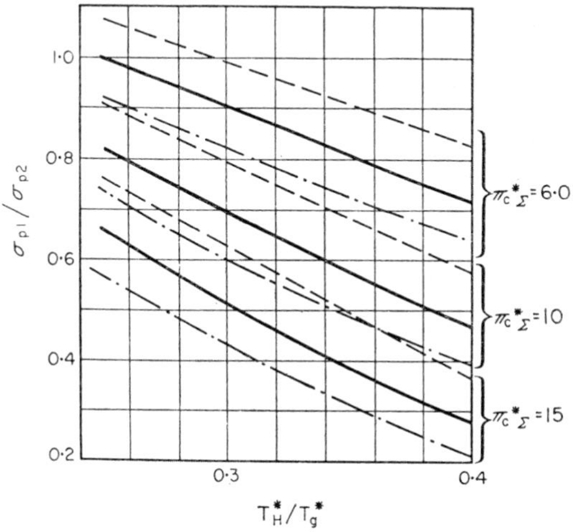

Fig. 36. Dependence of σ_{p1}/σ_{p2} on T^*_H/T^*_g.
—·—·— $\mu = 0{\cdot}4$;
——— $\mu = 0{\cdot}5$;
– – – $\mu = 0{\cdot}6$.

The relationship between the safety factors for the blades of the second and first stages can be written in the form

$$\frac{K\sigma_2}{K\sigma_1} = \frac{\sigma^{b_2}_{100}}{\sigma^{b_1}_{100}} \frac{q\lambda_{t2}}{q\lambda_{t1}} \frac{\sin\alpha_{t2}}{\sin\alpha_{t1}} \frac{1}{\pi^{*(n_t+1)/n_t}_{t_2}},$$

where σ_{100} is the endurance factor.

The curves of the endurance factor for heat-resistant alloys show that in the region of operating values of temperature of the blades the magnitude of σ_{100} obeys an approximately linear law. In connection with this we can write

$$\sigma^{b_2}_{100} = \sigma^{b_1}_{100} + K_0 \left(T_{b_1} - T_{b_2}\right).$$

After processing the experimental data a mean value is obtained for the coefficient $K_0 = 15{\cdot}3$. With the aid of the previous equation we also obtain

$$\frac{\sigma^{b_2}_{100}}{\sigma^{b_1}_{100}} = 1 + \frac{T_{b1}}{\sigma^{b_1}_{100}} K_0 \left(1 - \frac{T_{b2}}{T_{b1}}\right).$$

The temperature of the blades near the root can be coupled with the temperature of the retarded flow of the gas relative to the motion at the mean diameter by the relationship $T_b = \Theta T^*_w$, where

Θ takes into account the irregularity of distribution of the gas temperature around the radius, the removal of heat and the reduction of T_w^* on account of the reduction in the extent of the reaction in the root sections (reduction in u/c_{ad}^*). If it be assumed that the coefficient Θ is identical in both stages, then

$$\frac{T_{b2}}{T_{b1}} = \frac{T_{\omega 2}^*}{T_{\omega 1}^*}.$$

Consequently we obtain

$$\frac{\sigma_{100}^{b_2}}{\sigma_{100}^{b_1}} = 1 + \frac{T_{b1}}{\sigma_{100}^{b_1}} K_0 \left(1 - \frac{T_{\omega 2}^*}{T_{\omega 1}^*}\right).$$

The stresses corresponding to the endurance factor for the blades of the first stage can be connected with the stress corresponding to the endurance factor for the temperature, equal to the temperature of the gas prior to the turbine, by the following relationship:

$$\sigma_{100}^{b_1} = \sigma_{100}^{T_g^*} + K_0 T_g^* \left(1 - \Theta \frac{T_{\omega 1}^*}{T_g^*}\right),$$

where T_g^* is the temperature of the gas prior to the turbine.

Finally

$$\frac{K\sigma_2}{K\sigma_1} = \left[1 + \frac{T_{\omega 1}^*/T_g^*}{\dfrac{\sigma_{100}^{T_g^*}}{T_g^*} + K_0\left(1 - \Theta \dfrac{T_{\omega 1}^*}{T_g^*}\right)} K_0 \Theta \left(1 - \frac{T_{\omega 2}^*}{T_{\omega 1}^*}\right)\right] \times$$

$$\times \frac{q(\lambda_t)_2 \sin \alpha_{t2}}{q(\lambda_t)_1 \sin \alpha_{t1}} \frac{1}{\pi_{t2}^{*(n_t+1)/2n_t}}. \qquad (2.32)$$

The ratio T_{w1}^* / T_g^* can be expressed by the following equation, quoted for the condition $C_{2u} = 0$, which, however, gives a small error:

$$\frac{T_{\omega 1}^*}{T_g^*} = \left(\frac{u}{c_{\text{ad}}^*}\right)_1^2 \left(1 - \frac{1}{\pi_{t1}^{*(k_g-1)/k_g}}\right) + \frac{1}{\pi_{t1}^{*(n_t-1)/n_t}}.$$

This equation can be used also for the second stage by using the value of u/c_{ad}^* and π_t^* corresponding to this stage, assuming as T_g^* the gas temperature on discharge from the first stage T_{t1}^*.

Using the expressions for T_{w1}^* / T_g^* and T_{w2}^* / T_t^*, the relationship between T_{w2}^* and T_{w1}^* can be expressed in the following manner:

$$\frac{T^*_{\omega 2}}{T^*_{\omega 1}} = \frac{1}{\pi_{t1}^{*(n_t-1)/n_t}} \cdot \frac{\left(\frac{u}{c^*_{\text{ad}}}\right)_2\left(1-\frac{1}{\pi_{t2}^{*(k_g-1)/k_g}}\right)+\frac{1}{\pi_{t2}^{*(n_t-1)/n_t}}}{\left(\frac{u}{c^*_{\text{ad}}}\right)_1\left(1-\frac{1}{\pi_{t1}^{*(k_g-1)/k_g}}\right)+\frac{1}{\pi_{t1}^{*(n_t-1)/n_t}}}.$$

The ratio between u/c^*_{ad} of the second and first stages has the form

$$\frac{\left(\frac{u}{c^*_{\text{ad}}}\right)_2}{\left(\frac{u}{c^*_{\text{ad}}}\right)_1} = \frac{u_2}{u_1}\sqrt{\left(\pi_{t1}^{*(n_t-1)/n_t}\frac{1-1/\pi_{t1}^{*(k_g-1)/k_g}}{1-1/\pi_{t2}^{*(k_g-1)/k_g}}\right)}. \tag{2.33}$$

Figure 37 shows the dependence of $K_{\sigma 2}/K_{\sigma 1}$ on T^*_H/T^*_g for different values of π^*_c and μ. For calculation, it is taken that

$$\Theta=0{\cdot}95; \quad \frac{\sigma_{100}^{T^*_g}}{T^*_g}=2{\cdot}0; \quad \left(\frac{u}{c^*_{\text{ad}}}\right)_1=0{\cdot}55; \quad \frac{u_2}{u_1}=0{\cdot}95.$$

The blade material is assumed to be identical in both cases[1].

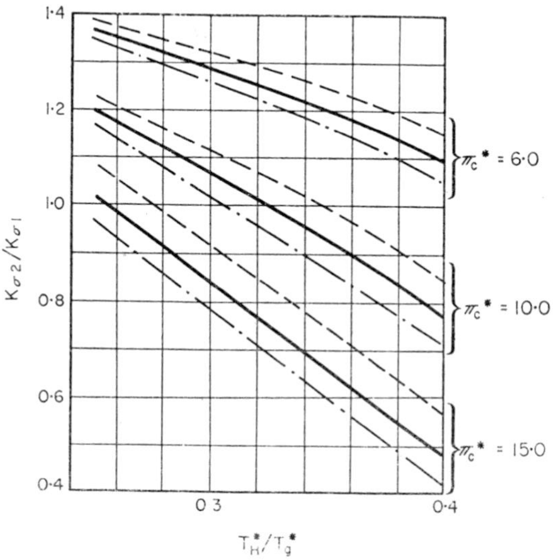

Fig. 37. Dependence of $K_{\sigma 2}/K_{\sigma 1}$ on T^*_H/T^*_g.
— — — $\mu = 0{\cdot}6$;
———— $\mu = 0{\cdot}5$;
—·—·— $\mu = 0{\cdot}4$.

[1] The ratio $\sigma_{100}^{T^*_g}/T^*_g = 2{\cdot}0$ is an average value, However, its variation over an actually possible range, has little effect on the quantitative results.

For $\pi_c^*=6{\cdot}0$ and for small ratios of T_H^*/T_g^* for other values of π_c^*, the safety factor for the blades of the second stage is greater than for the blades of the first stage, and which is characteristic for modern engines.

In the region of large values of T_H^*/T_g^* and $\pi_{c1}^*>6{\cdot}0$ the safety factor for the blades of the second stage of the turbine becomes less than for the blades of the first stage. It should be mentioned that on account of the bending stresses the relationships between the safety factors should be somewhat altered, but, since the tensile stresses are fundamental with respect to magnitude, the resulting general regularity should be conserved.

The Effect of Expansion Ratio and Gas Temperature on the Dimensions of the Compressor and of the Turbine

General aspects. As we have shown above, the diameter of the compressor can be expressed via the air flow rate and the efficiency factor

$$D_c=\sqrt{\left(\frac{4G_a\sqrt{(T_H^*)}}{\pi Sp_a^*G_c}\right)}$$

If the air flow rate be substituted by the thrust of the engine R and the specific thrust R_{sp}, then the previous equation takes the form

$$D_c=\sqrt{\left(\frac{4R\sqrt{(T_H^*)}}{\pi Sp_a^*R_{sp}\bar{G}_c}\right)}\ . \qquad (2.34)$$

The relationship between the diameter of the compressor and of the turbine is expressed by means of the equations presented above (2.30) and (2.31).

If follows from equation (2.34) that the ratio of the diameters of the compressors of both engines, possessing identical thrust for identical values of T_H^* and p_a^*, will be equal to

$$\frac{D_c}{D_{co}}=\sqrt{\left(\frac{R_{sp0}}{R_{sp}}\,\frac{\bar{G}_{co}}{\bar{G}_c}\right)}, \qquad (2.35)$$

where the index zero corresponds to a certain initial engine.

Thus, the relationship between the dimensions of the compressors of both engines is determined by the product of the specific thrust and the efficiency factor.

The relationship between the diameters of the turbines, as it follows from equations (2.31) and (2.35), will depend on the ratio of the diameters of the compressors and, consequently, on R_{sp} and $\overline{G}_c$, and, moreover, on other quantities entering into equation (2.31) for $\alpha_t = \text{const}$, we obtain

$$\frac{D_t}{D_{to}} = \frac{D_c}{D_{co}} \frac{\sqrt{\left(\frac{u_c^2}{\sigma_p}\right)_0}}{\sqrt{\left(\frac{u_c^2}{\sigma_p}\right)}} \frac{\frac{\xi_2}{X}+X}{\frac{\xi_2}{X_0}+X_0}. \tag{2.36}$$

However, sometimes the relationships between the sizes of the compressors and turbines are judged only by the magnitude of the specific thrust, which is applicable to the compressor, and corresponds to constancy of the value of the efficiency factor, independent of the parameters of the engine and, consequently to the equation

$$\frac{D_c}{D_{c0}} = \sqrt{\left(\frac{R_{sp.0}}{R_{sp}}\right)} . \tag{2.37}$$

The efficiency factor enters into the complex parameter $\varPi = u_c^2 \overline{G}_c / \sigma_P q(\lambda_t)$ being a function of π_c^* and T_H^* / T_g^*. Consequently, if it be assumed that $\overline{G}_c = \text{const.}$ then different values of $u_c^2 / \sigma_p q(\lambda_t)$ should be obtained in engines with different values of π_c^* and T_H^* / T_g^*.

This principle of comparison of the sizes of the turbo-compressor section of engines can be assumed proportional only in the case if, for a variation in $u_c^2 / \sigma_p q(\lambda_t)$, the quantities u_c, σ_p and λ_t will not go beyond the limits of permissible or rational values, which is practically impossible when T_H^* / T_g^* and π_c^* are varied over a wide range.

On the other hand, the dimensions of engines can be compared by using a constant value for $u_c^2 / \sigma_p q(\lambda_t)$. In this case the efficiency factor $\overline{G}_c$ will be changed just as the complex parameter is changed and therefore, for example, in place of equation (2.35) it is possible to write

$$\frac{D_c}{D_{c0}} = \sqrt{\left(\frac{R_{sp.0}}{R_{sp}} \frac{\varPi_0}{\varPi}\right)}. \tag{2.38}$$

Comparison for $\overline{G}_c = \text{const.}$, or for $u_c^2 / \sigma_p q(\lambda_t) = \text{const.}$ corresponds to two limiting cases, which are discussed in detail below.

Since for this there is no basis for assuming different values of λ_t for the engines being compared, then we shall assume that $q(\lambda_t) = \text{const.}$, and we shall consider as a parameter the quantity u_c^2/σ_p. Besides the cases for comparison mentioned, intermediate cases are possible, which are, however, less characteristic.

Comparison of dimensions for $\overline{G}_c = const.$ and for $u_c^2/\sigma_p = const.$, for cases when $\pi_c^* = const.$ and $T_H^*/T_g^* = var.$ In order to compare two basic methods of comparison of the dimensions of turbo-jet engines, we shall assume initially that the expansion ratio remains constant, but the ratio T_H^*/T_g^* varies. If the value of π_c^* is small ($\pi_c^* < 4{\cdot}0$) then, as can be seen from Fig. 28, the magnitude of the complex parameter varies insignificantly. Therefore comparison of the sizes of the compressors, just as for $\overline{G}_c = \text{const.}$, so also for $u_c^2/\sigma_p = \text{const.}$, will be little different over a wide range of values of π_H^*/I_g^*. The situation stands otherwise for higher values of π_c^*. In this case for variation of T_H^*/T_g^* the complex parameter also varies and therefore comparison for $\overline{G}_c = \text{const.}$ and for $u_c^2/\sigma_y = \text{const.}$, will lead to considerably different results. Thus for example, for a reduction in T_H^*/T_g^* the complex parameter increases and therefore for $u_c^2/\sigma_p = \text{const.}$, $\overline{G}_c$ increases[1] and, consequently, the ratio D_c/D_{co} will be less than for $\overline{G}_c = \text{const.}$

As a result of this the size of the turbine is reduced to the same extent as the size of the compressor, since u_c^2/σ_p and X will remain constant in equation (2.36).

In order to illustrate what has been said, let us take an example: in an engine with an expansion ratio of $\pi_c^* = 6{\cdot}0$ and a gas temperature of $T_g^* = 1220°$ K, for a flight/speed of $M_H = 2{\cdot}5$ at an altitude of H $\geq$ 11 km, the specific thrust is equal to 26·5 kg/kg sec and the parameter $\Pi = 42{\cdot}5$. If we take $u_c = 450$ m/sec, $\sigma_p = 2800$ kg/cm² and, $\lambda_t = 0{\cdot}6$, then the efficiency factor of the compressor, $\overline{G}_c = 0{\cdot}478$. For $d_t = 0{\cdot}7$, the ratio of the diameter of the compressor to the diameter of the turbine $D_c/D_t = 0{\cdot}891$. In the case of increase of the gas temperature to 1500°K, the specific thrust increases to 45 kg/kg sec and the parameter Π to 51·2. If u_c/σ_p and λ_t are maintained unchanged, then the efficiency factor of the compressor $\overline{G}_k$ in creases to 0·577, but the ratio D_c/D_t will also be equal to 0·891. If the

[1] Here and henceforth it is supposed that the initial value of $\overline{G}_{co}$ is less than $G_{c.max}$.

diameters of the compressors are compared for $\overline{G}_c$=const., then their ratio will be 0·77 and it is further reduced by 10 per cent if the comparison is made for u_c^2/σ_p =const., i.e. when $\overline{G}_c$ =var., Since in this case the ratio $D_t/D_{t0}=D_c/D_{c0}$, then, consequently, the diameter of the turbine is also reduced correspondingly. Thus, the effect of $\overline{G}_c$ in the example under consideration is quite considerable.

It should be noted that the result obtained is independent of the fact that the values of u_c and σ_p will be maintained unchanged either as a result of changing T_g^* from 1200°K to 1500°K or for u_c^2/σ_p=const., on account of improvement in the blade material or by cooling them or further by reducing σ_p and u_c correspondingly. The latter has an effect primarily on changing the number of stages or on their stresses. At the same time, it is necessary to point out that an increase in $\overline{G}_c$ for M=2·5 involves a certain narrowing of the operating range of the engine for constant r.p.m.

*Comparison of Dimensions for G_k=const. and for u_c^2/σ_p=const. for the case when T_H^*/T_g^*=const. and π_c^*=*var. For a constant ratio T_H^*/T_g^* and a variable expansion ratio, the complex parameter as was discussed above, has a maximum value for a certain value of π_c^*.

Figure 38 shows the optimum values of π_c^*, calculated according to equation (2.14); similarly the expansion ratios are plotted, corresponding to the maximum values of the specific thrust for certain values of $\delta\pi_V$.

It can be seen from Fig. 38 that the optimum expansion ratio corresponding to the maximum value of the complex parameter is considerably higher in magnitude than those of π_c^*, which correspond to $R_{\text{sp max}}$ and especially in the region of small ratios of T_H^*/T_g^*. It should be noted at the same time that π_c^*, corresponding to $\Pi_{\max}$ practically coincides with the values of the expansion ratios for which the maximum specific thrust is achieved in a turbo-jet engine with the use of a reheat chamber, to which attention has already been paid above.

If it be assumed that for a comparison of dimensions $\overline{G}_c$=const. is maintained, then the quantity u_c^2/σ_p should vary the same as the complex parameter, i.e. it should increase for increase in π_c^* until such time as the complex parameter attains a maximum. It is obvious that the efficiency factor $\overline{G}_c$ will be similarly changed, if the condition that u_c^2/σ_p=const. is imposed for the comparison

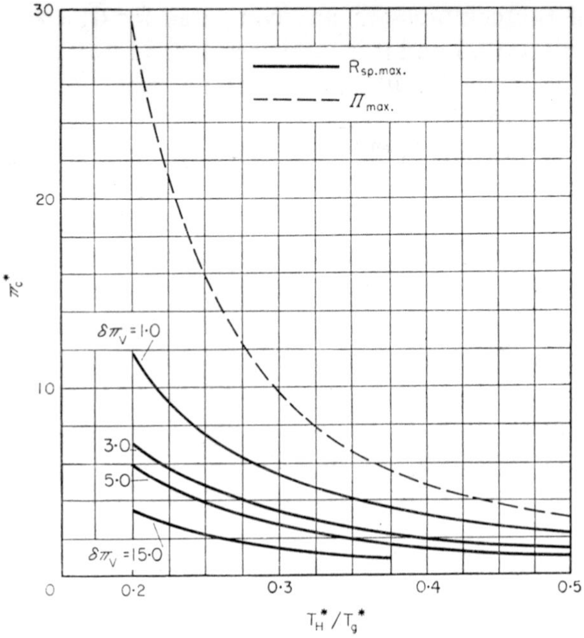

Fig. 38. Variation of expansion ratio for $R_{sp\ max}$ and Π_{max} for $\eta_c^* = 0{\cdot}83$ and $\eta_t^* = 0{\cdot}91$.

of dimensions. In the latter case the minimum dimensions of the compressor in a turbo-jet engine without the use of a reheat chamber should occur when the maximum is the product $R_{sp}\bar{G}_c$ or $R_{sp}\ \Pi$ and, consequently, the equation

$$\frac{R'_{sp}}{R_{sp}} = -\frac{\Pi'}{\Pi}$$

should be fulfilled, where R'_{sp} and Π' are the partial derivatives of R_{sp} and Π with respect to π_c^*. The expansion ratio satisfying this equation will have an intermediate value between π_c^*, corresponding to $R_{sp\ max}$ and Π_{max}. Moreover, it is extremely important to note that for high flight speeds the expansion ratios corresponding to Π_{max}, either differ relatively slightly from π_c^*, corresponding to the optimum gas temperature according to efficiency, or even exceed them. Therefore, by carrying out an appraisal of the methods of comparison of dimensions for $\bar{G}_k = \text{const.}$ or for $u_c^2/\sigma_p = \text{const.}$ for the case when $T_H^*/T_g^* = \text{const.}$ and $\pi_c^* = \text{var.}$, it is advantageous to consider primarily only the region in which the complex parameter increases as a result of an increase in π_c^*, since a further increase in π_c^* after attaining Π_{max} does not present any practical interest. In considering the method of comparison of dimensions for $\overline{G}_c$=const., it should be noted that in this case, in contrast to the condition u_c^2/σ_p=const., the possibility of increase of $\overline{G}_c$ according to the extent of increase of π_c^* is not utilized; meanwhile, in certain circumstances an increase in $\overline{G}_c$ and a reduction in dimensions may present interest.

In order to illustrate quantitatively the principle of comparison for u_c^2/σ_p=const., we shall establish the dependence of σ_p on π_c^*. Let us consider first of all single-stage turbines which may be used for relatively small values of π_c^* in the region where $\Pi<\Pi_{max}$. If, originally, a certain value $\pi_c^*=\pi_{co}^*$ be assumed, then for an identical safety factor with respect to tensile stresses, the ratio of these stresses in the turbine under consideration and in the original turbine is written down in the form

$$\frac{\sigma_p}{\sigma_{p0}}=\frac{\sigma_{100}^{b}}{\sigma_{100}^{0b}}\,.$$

Expressing σ_{100}^b and σ_{100}^{0b} by $\sigma_{100}^{T_g^*}$, we obtain

$$\frac{\sigma_p}{\sigma_{p0}}=\frac{\dfrac{\sigma_{100}^{T_g^*}}{T_g^*}+K_0\left(1-\Theta\dfrac{T_\omega^*}{T_g^*}\right)}{\dfrac{\sigma_{100}^{T_g^*}}{T_g^*}+K_0\left(1-\Theta\dfrac{T_{\omega 0}^*}{T_g^*}\right)} \qquad (2.39)$$

where

$$\frac{T_\omega^*}{T_g^*}=\left(\frac{u}{c_{ad}^*}\right)_0^2\left(1-\frac{1}{\pi_t^{*(k_g-1)/k_g}}\right)+\frac{1}{\pi_t^{*(n_t-1)/n}}\,;$$

$$\frac{T_{\omega 0}^*}{T_g^*}=\left(\frac{u}{c_{ad}^*}\right)_0^2\left(1-\frac{1}{\pi_{to}^{*(k_g-1)/k_g}}\right)+\frac{1}{\pi_{to}^{*(n_t-1)/n_t}}\,.$$

In connection with the small effect of the first term on the ratios T_ω^*/T_g^* and $T_{\omega o}^*/T_g^*$ it can be assumed that u/c_{ad}^* is identical for all values of π_c^*, although the designing of a turbine to satisfy this condition does not always prove to be possible.

Figure 39 shows the dependence of σ_p/σ_{po} on T_H^*/T_g^* for various values of π_c^* and for the condition $\pi_{co}^*=4{\cdot}0$.

For the calculations it is assumed that $\sigma_{100}/T_g^* = 2{\cdot}0$,[1] $u/c_{ad}^* = 0{\cdot}55$, $x = 0{\cdot}95$, $\eta_t^* = 0{\cdot}91$ and $\eta_c^* = 0{\cdot}83$. It can be seen from Fig. 39 that for an increase in π_c^* there is the possibility of increasing σ_p in consequence of the reduction in the temperature of the blades. Therefore, for $u_c^2/\sigma_p = \text{const.}$ it is also possible to increase u_c, or by maintaining u_c and σ_p invariable to obtain an increase in the safety factor.

In order to illustrate what has been said, we shall carry out a comparison of the dimensions of engines with expansion ratios of $\pi_c^* = 2{\cdot}5$ and $\pi_c^* = 4{\cdot}0$ for identical gas temperature $T_g^* = 1220°\text{K}$

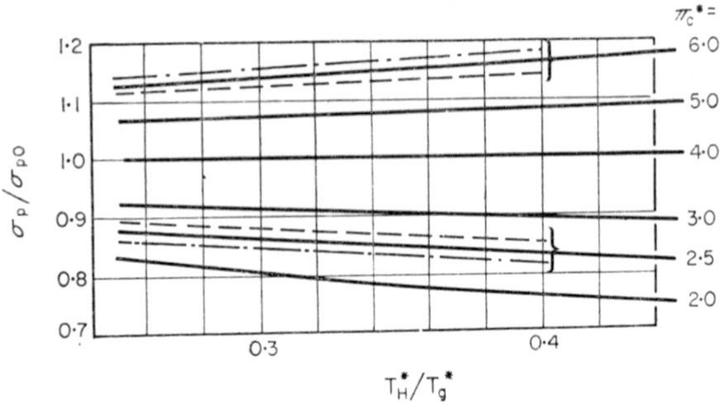

Fig. 39. Dependence of σ_p/σ_{p0} for single-stage turbines on T_H^*/T_g^* and π_c^*.

— — — $\sigma_{100}/T_g^* = 2{\cdot}5$;

———— $\sigma_{100}/T_g^* = 2{\cdot}0$;

—·—·— $\sigma_{100}/T_g^* = 1{\cdot}5$.

and a flight velocity corresponding to $M_H = 2{\cdot}5$ $(T_H^*/T_g^* = 0{\cdot}4)$. We shall take for the engine with an expansion ratio of $\pi_c^* = 2{\cdot}5$ the following values for the coefficients: $\eta_c^* = 0{\cdot}83$, $\eta_t^* = 0{\cdot}91$, $\delta_\Sigma = 0{\cdot}7$. Hence we obtain $R_{sp} = 36{\cdot}9$ kg/kg sec and $\Pi = 39{\cdot}7$. If we choose $u_c = 415$ m/sec, $\sigma_p = 2350$ kg/cm² and $\lambda_t = 0{\cdot}6$, then we obtain $G_c = 0{\cdot}445$ and $u_c^2/\sigma_p = 72{\cdot}5$. In order to assess the required speed of the turbine we assume that $Y^* = u_{av}/c_{ad}^* = 0{\cdot}55$. This value of Y^* corresponds to $u_{av} = 339$ m/sec. Evaluating X we find, according to equation (2·31), that $D_c/D_t = 0{\cdot}995$ and $u_t = 417$ m sec. From equation (2·30) we find that $\bar{d}_t = 0{\cdot}625$.

[1] Fig. 39 shows the variation of σ_p/σ_{p0} for certain values of π_c^* and also for $\sigma_{100}/T_g^* = 1{\cdot}5$ and $2{\cdot}5$, which indicates the relatively small effect of this ratio.

For an expansion ratio of $\pi_c^*=4{\cdot}0$, for the same efficiencies and pressure coefficients we obtain: $R_{sp}=32{\cdot}2$ kg/kg sec and $\Pi=43{\cdot}5$ Retaining λ_t and u_c^2/σ_p we obtain $\overline{G}_c=0{\cdot}49$.

It can be seen from Fig. 39 that the ratio of the stresses in the turbine blades for $\lambda_c=2{\cdot}5$ and $\lambda_c=4{\cdot}0$, for identical safety factors, will be 0·84. Therefore, the stress for $\pi_c^*=4{\cdot}0$ will amount to 2800 kg/cm². To this stress corresponds a peripheral speed for the compressor of $u_c=450$ m/sec. If in the given case it be assumed that $Y^*=0{\cdot}55$, then $u_{av}=434$ m/sec. Further, the ratio $D_c/D_t=0{\cdot}891$, but $u_t=505$ m/sec and $\overline{d}_t=0{\cdot}715$.

In the case when, for $\pi_c^*=4{\cdot}0$, the peripheral speed of the compressor u_c and the stresses σ_p are maintained the same magnitude as for $\pi_c^*=2{\cdot}5$, the safety factor in the turbine blades increases by approximately 19 per cent.

In comparing the compressor diameters resulting only from the specific thrust, we obtain that the diameter of the compressor for $\pi_c^*=4{\cdot}0$ should be 7 per cent greater than the diameter for $\pi_c^*=$ $=2{\cdot}5$. If, further, the variation of the efficiency factor be taken into consideration, then it is necessary to increase the diameter of the compressor for $\pi_c^*=4{\cdot}0$ in all by 1·5 per cent. Further, the diameter of the turbine increases by approximately 13 per cent.

Comparison of diameters with respect to the magnitude of R_{sp} corresponds to the condition $\overline{G}_c=$const. If for $\pi_c^*=4{\cdot}0$ one assumes the same efficiency factor as for $\pi_c^*=2{\cdot}5$, and if one supposes, as before, that σ_p increases to $\sigma_p=2800$ kg/cm², then the dimensions and parameters of the turbine do not alter, but the peripheral speed of the compressor increases to 475 m/sec, which is an extremely high value.

The example presented confirms that even for a relatively small increase in π_c^* the dimensions of the compressor are noticeably reduced, if u_c^2/σ_p be maintained constant. As a result of further increase of π_c^* to a value corresponding to Π_{max}, it may be necessary to use a turbine with two or more stages.

As shown above, limitations with respect to safety factor in a two-stage turbine may be imposed by the blades of the first or second stage, dependent upon π_c^* and the ratio T_H^*/T_g^*. Therefore, the permissible value of σ_{p2} for the second stage, which enters into the complex parameter Π, will be determined either by the first or by the second stage of the turbine.

The admissibility of the variation of σ_{p2} in relation to π_c^* and T_H^*/T_g^* is conveniently shown by comparing the r.p.m.[1] of an engine with a two-stage turbine with the r.p.m. of a turbo-jet engine having the same air flow rate and a single-stage turbine for some fixed value of $\pi_c^* = \pi_{co}^*$.

The tensile stresses in the blades of the first stage can be written down in the form

$$\sigma_{p1} = 3{\cdot}86 \times 10^{-4} n^2 G_g \frac{\sqrt{(T_g^*)}}{p_g^*} \frac{\pi_{t1}^{*\,(n_t+1)/2n_t} \Phi}{q(\lambda_t)_1 \sin\alpha_{t1} S}.$$

For the blades of the second stage we obtain correspondingly

$$p_2 = 3{\cdot}86 \times 10^{-4} n^2 G_g \frac{\sqrt{(T_g^*)}}{p_g^*} \frac{\pi_{t\Sigma}^{*\,(n_t+1)/2n_t} \Phi}{q(\lambda_t)_2 \sin\alpha_{t2} S}.$$

For the engine with a single-stage turbine we have

$$\sigma_{p0} = 3{\cdot}86 \times 10^{-4} n_0^2 G_{g0} \frac{\sqrt{(T_{g0}^*)}}{p_{g0}^*} \frac{\pi_{t0}^{*\,(n_t+1)/2n_t} \Phi}{q(\lambda_{t0}) \sin\alpha_{t0} S}.$$

The ratio of the safety factor in the blades of the single-stage turbine to the safety factor in the blades of the first stage, for identical temperature of the gas in the combustion chamber and identical supply of air and shape factor Φ, can be written down in the following manner:

$$\frac{K_{\sigma 0}}{K_{\sigma 1}} = \frac{\sigma_{100}^{0b}}{\sigma_{100}^{b1}} \frac{n^2}{n_0^2} \frac{\pi_{c0}^*}{\pi_c^*} \left(\frac{\pi_{t1}^*}{\pi_{t0}^*}\right)^{(n_t+1)/2n_t} \frac{q(\lambda_t)_0 \sin\alpha_{t0}}{q(\lambda_t)_1 \sin\alpha_{t1}}. \quad (2.40)$$

Similarly for the blades of the second stage we have, assuming that

$$q(\lambda_t)_2 \sin\alpha_{t_2} = q(\lambda_t)_0 \sin\alpha_{t0},$$

$$\frac{K_{\sigma 0}}{K_{\sigma 1}} = \frac{\pi_{100}^{0b}}{\pi_{100}^{b2}} \frac{n^2}{n_0^2} \frac{\pi_{c0}^*}{n_c^*} \left(\frac{\pi_{t\Sigma}^*}{\pi_{t0}^*}\right)^{(n_t+1)/2n_t}. \quad (2.41)$$

If it be assumed that $K_{\sigma 0}/K_{\sigma 1} = 1{\cdot}0$ and $K_{\sigma 0}/K_{\sigma 2} = 1{\cdot}0$, then it is possible to find from these equations the relationship between the r.p.m's, which will also characterize the limitations imposed by the first or second stage of a two-stage turbine.

[1] Strictly speaking, the products $n^2 G_a$ should be compared, where G_a is the air flow rate through the engine, depending for a given thrust on π_c^* and T_g^*. However, the numerical results remain unchanged.

Expressing σ_{100}^{ob}; $\sigma_{100}^{b_1}$; $\sigma_{100}^{b_2}$ by $\sigma_{100}^{T_g^*}$, corresponding to the temperature of the gas prior to the turbine, we obtain the following equation for n/n_0, arising from the equality of the safety factors in the blades of the first stage and in the blades of the single-stage turbine:

$$\left(\frac{n}{n_0}\right)^2 = \frac{\dfrac{\sigma_{100}^{T_g^*}}{T_g^*} + k_0\left(1-\Theta\dfrac{T_{\omega 1}^*}{T_g^*}\right)}{\dfrac{\sigma_{100}^{T_g^*}}{T_g^*} + k_0\left(1-\Theta\dfrac{T_{\omega 0}^*}{T_g^*}\right)} \frac{\pi_c^*}{\pi_{k0}^*}\left(\frac{\pi_{t\,0}^*}{\pi_{t\,1}^*}\right)^{(n_t+1)/2n_t} \frac{q(\lambda_t)_1 \sin\alpha_{t1}}{q(\lambda_t)_0 \sin\alpha_{t0}}. \tag{2.42}$$

Correspondingly we obtain for the second stage

$$\left(\frac{n}{n_0}\right)^2 = \frac{\dfrac{\sigma_{100}^{T_g^*}}{T_g^*} + k_0\left(1-\Theta\dfrac{T_{\omega 2}^*}{T_{g1}^*}\dfrac{1}{\pi_{t\,2}^{*\,(n_t+1)/n_t}}\right)}{\dfrac{\sigma_{100}^{T_g^*}}{T_g^*} + k_0\left(1-\Theta\dfrac{T_{\omega 0}^*}{T_g^*}\right)} \frac{\pi_c^*}{\pi_{c0}^*}\left(\frac{\pi_{t\,0}^*}{\pi_{t\,\Sigma}^*}\right)^{(n_t+1)/2n_t}. \tag{2.43}$$

We determine n/n_0 according to equations (2.42) and (2.43) and for given values of π_c^* and T_H^*/T_g^* we shall take the least value of n/n_0.

Thus, we make it possible to determine the ratio of the stress in the blades of the second stage of the turbine to the stress in the blades of the single-stage turbine

$$\frac{\sigma_{p2}}{\sigma_{p0}} = \frac{n^2}{n_0^2}\frac{\pi_{c0}^*}{\pi_c^*}\left(\frac{\pi_{t\,\Sigma}^*}{\pi_{t\,0}^*}\right)^{(n_t+1)/2n_t}. \tag{2.44}$$

This ratio, as already mentioned, will also characterize the variation in σ_p, which enters into the complex parameter.

Figure 40 shows the results of calculations with respect to the determination of σ_{p2}/σ_{p0}. It has been assumed in the calculations that $\Theta=0{\cdot}95$; $\sigma_{100}^{T_g^*}/T_g^*=1{\cdot}5$; $2{\cdot}0$; $2{\cdot}5$[1], the efficiency of tbe turbine $\eta_t^*=0{\cdot}91$ and the efficiency of the compressor $\eta_c^*=0{\cdot}83$ for all values of π_c^*. For the first stage of the turbine it is assumed that:

$$\frac{u}{c_{ad}^*} = 0{\cdot}55\,, \quad \frac{L_{ad\cdot t1}^*}{L_{ad\cdot t\Sigma}^*} = 0{\cdot}5 \text{ and } \frac{q(\lambda_t)_1 \sin\alpha_{t1}}{q(\lambda_t)_0 \sin\alpha_{t0}} = \frac{1}{1{\cdot}5}\,.$$

[1] The values of $\sigma_{100}/T_g^* = 1{\cdot}5$ and $2{\cdot}5$ are given only for $\pi_c^* = 4{\cdot}0$, 8, 12 and 15.

For turbo-jet engines with a single-stage turbine, the expansion ratio $\pi_{co}^{*} = 4{\cdot}0$ for all values of T_H^*/T_g^* and $u/c_{ad}^* = 0{\cdot}55$.

The lines for Π_{max} are plotted in the same figure.

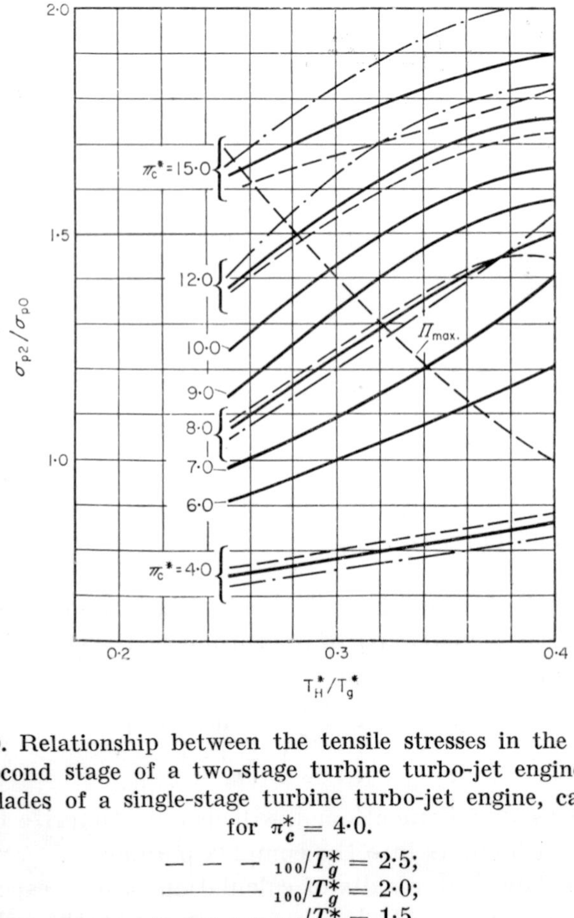

Fig. 40. Relationship between the tensile stresses in the blades of the second stage of a two-stage turbine turbo-jet engine and in the blades of a single-stage turbine turbo-jet engine, calculated for $\pi_c^* = 4{\cdot}0$.

— — — $_{100}/T_g^* = 2{\cdot}5$;
———— $_{100}/T_g^* = 2{\cdot}0$;
— · — · — $_{100}/T_g^* = 1{\cdot}5$.

It follows from Fig. 40 that the increase in π_c^* as a result of using a two-stage turbine leads to an increase in the permissible value of σ_p.

If only the region be considered where $\Pi < \Pi_{max}$, then in accordance with Fig. 40 there will only be a substantial increase in σ_{p2}/σ_{p0} for relatively small values of T_H^*/T_g^*, to which may correspond high values of the gas temperature. Thus for example, engines with an expansion ratio of $\pi_c^* = 6$ will be found in the region of $\Pi < \Pi_{max}$ (see Fig. 39) only in the case when $T_H^*/T_g^* < 0{\cdot}36$. For $M_H = 3{\cdot}0$, the value of $T_H^*/T_g^* = 0{\cdot}36$ will correspond to a gas temperature of $T_g^* = 1670°K$, and for $M_H = 2{\cdot}5$, $T_g = 1350°K$.

Since for the conditions mentioned, the blades of the turbine should be cooled, then an increase in σ_p with an increase in π_c^* can be limited because of the increased losses associated with cooling.

In considering for $T_H^*/T_g^* =$ const. and $\pi_c^* =$ var., the relationship between the diameter of the compressor and the turbine, it should be pointed out that in accordance with equation (2.31) this relationship for $u_c^2/\delta_p =$ const. will be determined only by change of magnitude of X, which, with increase in π_c^*, will increase at the expense of c_{ad}^*, if the increase in σ_p does not compensate the increase in c_{ad}^* and the number of stages remains invariable.

From the example presented above for $\pi_c^* = 2{\cdot}5$ and $4{\cdot}0$, and from Fig. 44, discussed in the following subdivision, it follows that in this case a complete compensation does not occur, as a consequence of which, with increase in π_c^*, the ratio D_c/D_t is decreased, i.e. the diameter of the turbine increases relatively more rapidly than the diameter of the compressor.

Results of the comparison of the dimensions of the compressor and of the turbine of engines for various values of π_c^* and T_H^*/T_g^*. The relationship between the dimensions of the compressor for both methods of comparison (i.e. for $\bar{G}_c =$ const. and for $u_c^2/\sigma_p =$ const.) is shown in Figs. 41, 42 and 43 over a wide range of values of π, and T_H^*/T_g^* for flight velocities corresponding to $M_H = 1{\cdot}0$; $2{\cdot}5$ and $3{\cdot}0$.

The values of the diameters for $M_H = 1{\cdot}0$ are related to its value for π_c^* corresponding to $R_{sp\,max}$ and $T_H^*/T_g^* = 0{\cdot}30$, and consequently for this M_H number, $R_{sp0} = R_{sp\,max}$.

For $M_H = 2{\cdot}5$ and $3{\cdot}0$, the values of the diameters are related to its value for $\pi_c^* = 2{\cdot}0$ and the ratio T_H^*/T_g^* correspondingly to $0{\cdot}4$ and $0{\cdot}5$, in connection with the fact that the maximum specific thrust according to Formula (1·66) for T_H^*/T_g^*, equal to $0{\cdot}4$ and $0{\cdot}5$, corresponds to $\pi_c^* \leq 1{\cdot}0$. It has been assumed in the calculations that the efficiency of the compressor, of the turbine and the pressure coefficient along the duct for all parameters at one and the same M_H, are identical. The comparison has been carried out for two cases, i.e. $u_c^2/\sigma_P =$ const. or $\bar{G}_c =$ var. only in the region where $\Pi <$

$\Pi_{\lim}$, In the region where $\Pi\,\Pi \geq_{\lim}$,[1] it was assumed that $\bar{G}_c = \bar{G}_{c.\max} = \text{const}$.

In addition, it was assumed that in the engines under comparison the values of the shape factors of the blades Φ and the angles of flow on discharge from the turbine α_t are identical.

Since the ratio of the diameters depends upon the ratio of the efficiency factors, which were determined by means of equation (2.10), then the quantity $u_c^2/\sigma_p\, q\,(\lambda_t)$ and also the shape factor Φ and the angle α_t, identical for the engines being compared, did not enter into the calculations and consequently the values of D_c in the curves presented in Figs. 41,42 and 43 did not depend on their absolute values. Let us consider the dependence of $\bar{D}_c$ on π_c^* for $M_H = 1{\cdot}0$ (see Fig. 41). The values of $\bar{D}_c$ are given for π_c^* from 4 to 50 and for values of T_H^*/T_g^* from 0·3 to 0·2. For $M_H = 1{\cdot}0$ the ratios of T_H^*/T_g^* are small, even for the gas temperatures in modern engines and the more so in the case of increase in T_g^*. Therefore, at sufficiently high values of π_c^* the calculated regimes of a turbo-jet engine will correspond to the region where $\Pi \geqslant \Pi_{\lim}$ and, consequently, $\bar{G}_c = \bar{G}_{c.\max}$.

In Fig. 41, the value of $\Pi = 70{\cdot}4$ is taken as limiting, to which, in accordance with Figs. 28 and 29, correspond values of $T_H^*/T_g^* \leq \leq 0{\cdot}25$ and $7 < \pi_c^* < 20$.[2]

This zone embraces a wide class of engines and, consequently, comparison of the dimensions of turbo-jet engines for $M_H = 1{\cdot}0$ should be mainly carried out with respect to magnitude of the specific thrust for maximum efficiency factor. Further, the region in which variation of the efficiency factor should be taken into account corresponds to parameters which do not present any significant interest, as can be seen from Fig. 41. If, further, a lower value for $\Pi_{\lim}$, be assumed, by reducing for example the peripheral speed of the compressor, then a considerable part of these parameters will fall into the zone where $\Pi \geq \Pi_{\text{lm}}$.

What has been said will also be related to a considerable extent to the flight speeds corresponding to $M_H \leq 1{\cdot}5 - 1{\cdot}7$, for which, in

[1] By the limiting value of Π is understood its arbitrary value corresponding to those values of the individual quantities entering into the complex parameter and, in particular, of $\bar{G}_c$, which can be assumed to be close to maximum.

[2] Data according to Fig. 29. are given for $\eta_c^*\eta_t^* = 0{\cdot}755$.

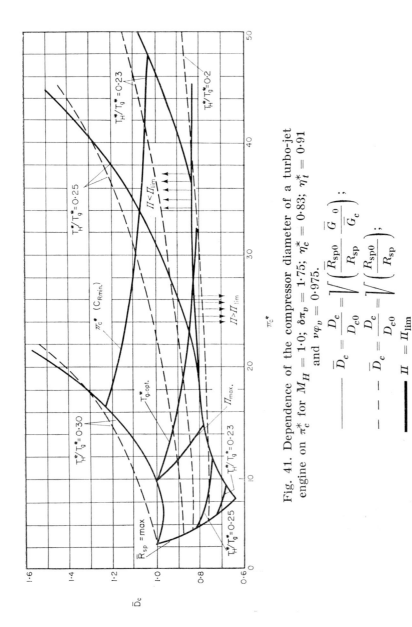

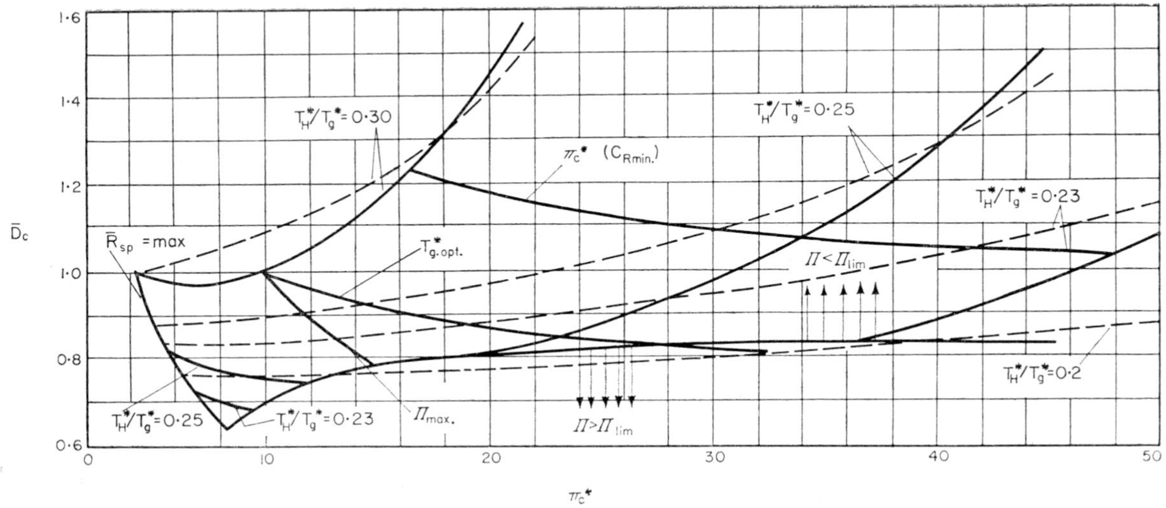

Fig. 41. Dependence of the compressor diameter of a turbo-jet engine on π_c^* for $M_H = 1·0$; $\delta\pi_v = 1·75$; $\eta_c^* = 0·83$; $\eta_t^* = 0·91$ and $\nu\varphi_v = 0·975$.

——— $\bar{D}_c = \dfrac{D_c}{D_{c0}} = \sqrt{\left(\dfrac{\bar{R}_{sp0}}{R_{sp}} \dfrac{\bar{G}_{0}}{\bar{G}_c}\right)}$;

– – – $\bar{D}_c = \dfrac{D_c}{D_{c0}} = \sqrt{\left(\dfrac{R_{sp0}}{R_{sp}}\right)}$;

▬▬ $\Pi = \Pi_{lim}$

practice, the least important values of T_H^*/T_g^* and π_c^* will also be found in the zone where $\Pi \geq \Pi_{\text{lim}}$.

This problem is different for the high supersonic flight speeds $M_H = 2{\cdot}5$ and $M_H = 3{\cdot}0$, for which the relative values of the compressor diameters are shown in Figs. 42 and 43. In this case, for all practically possible parameters, the values of Π are less than Π_{lim}. Therefore, comparison of the dimensions is more accurately carried out by taking into account the variation of the efficiency factor of the compressor, resulting from the principles discussed above.

It can be seen from Figs. 42 and 43 that for all values of T_H^*/T_g^* the magnitude of $\bar{D}_c$, obtained by taking into account the variation in $\bar{G}_c$, has lower values over a certain range of π_c^*, than as a result of comparison only with respect to the magnitude of the specific thrust. The lower T_H^*/T_g^* (i.e. the higher the temperature of the gas), the greater is the gain obtained in the dimensions and, at the

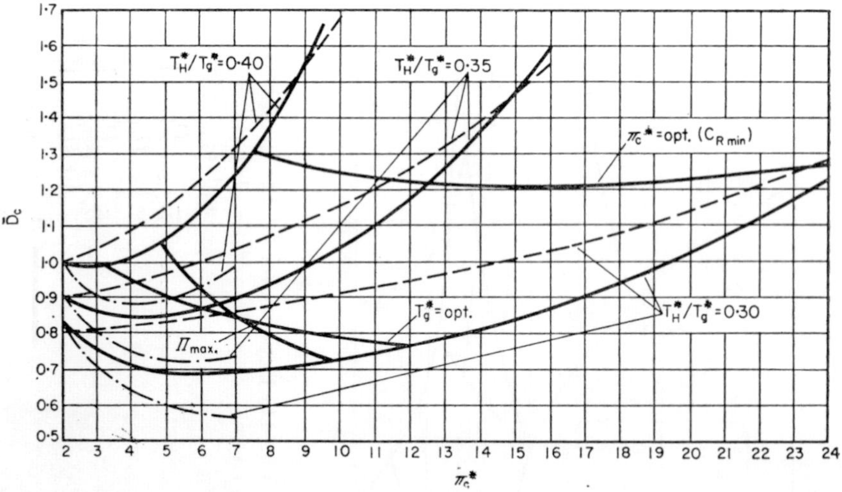

Fig. 42. Dependence of the compressor diameter of a turbo-jet engine on π_c^* for $M_H = 2{\cdot}5$; $\delta\pi_v = 12{\cdot}0$; $\eta_c^* = 0{\cdot}83$; $\eta_t^* = 0{\cdot}91$; and $\nu\varphi_v = 0{\cdot}975$.

———— $\bar{D}_c = \sqrt{\left(\dfrac{R_{\text{sp}0}}{R_{\text{sp}}}\,\dfrac{\bar{G}_{c0}}{\bar{G}_c}\right)}$;

— · — · — $\bar{D}_c = \sqrt{\left(\dfrac{R_{\text{sp}0}}{R_{\text{sp}}}\right)}$;

— — — — $\bar{D}_c = \sqrt{\left(\dfrac{R_{\text{sp}0}}{R_{\text{sp}}}\,\dfrac{\Pi_0}{\Pi}\,\dfrac{\sigma_{\text{p}0}}{\sigma_{\text{p}}}\right)}$.

same time, the range of expansion ratios is extended, within the limits of which this gain occurs. Moreover, as already mentioned, for a reduction in T^*_H/T^*_g for fixed values of π^*_c, the diameter of the turbine will be reduced to the same extent as will be the diameter of the compressor. Such an effect of the gas temperature on the dimensions of the compressor and of the turbine gives an additional argument for the advantage of increasing it, which was always disregarded earlier.

In Figs. 42 and 43 are also plotted the results of calculations carried out by taking into account the increase in σ_p according to the extent of increase in π^*_c, but for constant peripheral speed. In this

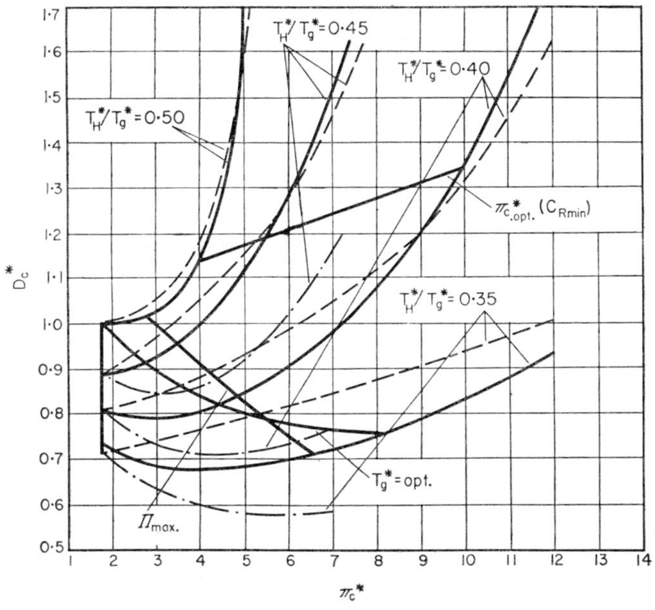

Fig. 43. Dependence of the compressor diameter of a turbo-jet engine on π^*_c, for $M_H = 3{\cdot}0$; $\delta\pi_v = 25$; $\eta^*_c = 0{\cdot}83$; $\eta^*_t = 0{\cdot}91$; and $\nu\varphi_v = 0{\cdot}975$.

——— $\bar{D}_c = \sqrt{\left(\frac{R_{sp0}}{R_{sp}} \frac{\bar{G}_{c0}}{\bar{G}_c}\right)}$;

– – – $\bar{D}_c = \sqrt{\left(\frac{R_{sp0}}{R_{sp}}\right)}$;

–·–·– $\bar{D}_c = \sqrt{\left(\frac{R_{sp0}}{R_{sp}} \frac{\Pi_0}{\Pi} \frac{\sigma_{p0}}{\sigma_p}\right)}$.

case the value of $\bar{D}_c$ is considerably less, since the increase in σ_p is utilized for increasing $\bar{G}_c$.

It should not be forgotten, however, that on account of the characteristics of the engine such an increase in $\bar{G}_c$ may not always prove to be admissible.

It can be seen from Figs. 42 and 43 that for practically all ratios of T^*_H/T^*_g for $\pi^*_c < \pi_c$, corresponding to $\Pi_{\max}$, there is a minimum value for the diameter $\bar{D}_c$. With increase of the gas temperature, the value of π^*_c also increases, corresponding to $\bar{D}_{c.\min}$. It is extremely important to note that the expansion ratio, corresponding to $\bar{D}_{c.\min}$, is relatively little different from the value of π^*_c, for which the temperature under discussion is optimum with respect to the efficiency (see the curves for $T^*_{g.\mathrm{opt}}$ in Figs. 42 and 43). Consequently, when the efficiency for a given engine has a prevailing value, the use of values of π^*_c corresponding to or close to those values for which the selected gas temperature will be optimum with respect to efficiency, will not lead to a significant increase in the dimensions of the compressor. However, the dimensions of the turbine will increase.

It can also be seen from Figs. 42 and 43 that for values of π which are optimum with respect to efficiency, the diametrical dimensions of the engine are very strongly increased and this is an additional argument against the use of such expansion ratios, about which mention has already been made earlier.

When a reheat chamber is used in a turbo-jet engine, the specific thrust depends relatively slightly on π^*_c and T^*_g. Therefore, in a turbo-jet engine with reheat chamber the change of the compressor dimensions will depend primarily on the change in the efficiency factor.

Therefore, in order to determine the relationship between the diameters of the compressors for various parameters, the curves shown in Figs. 28 and 29 can be used, which, for the condition that $u_c^2/\sigma_p\, q\,(\lambda_t) = \text{const.}$, also characterize the variation in $\bar{G}_c$.

The parameters corresponding to the minimum value of $\bar{D}_c$ will, in this case, coincide with the parameters corresponding to $\Pi_{\max}$.

As already mentioned above, the maximum value for the specific thrust of a turbo-jet engine with reheat chamber is also achieved as a result of this.

It should be mentioned that the data presented in Figs. 42 and 43 are calculated for all expansion ratios at constant values of the efficiencies of the compressor and of the turbine, which, taking into consideration the wide range of variation of π_c^*, is arbitrary, and for the most part with respect to the efficiency of the compressor.

As a result of reducing the efficiency, the dimensions calculated with respect to R_{sp} and taking into account the variation in $\bar{G}_c$ will converge among themselves in connection with the reduction in Π and $\bar{G}_c$.

Figure 44 shows the variation in D_t/D_c for $M_H = 2{\cdot}5$ as a result of using a single-stage and a two-stage turbine.

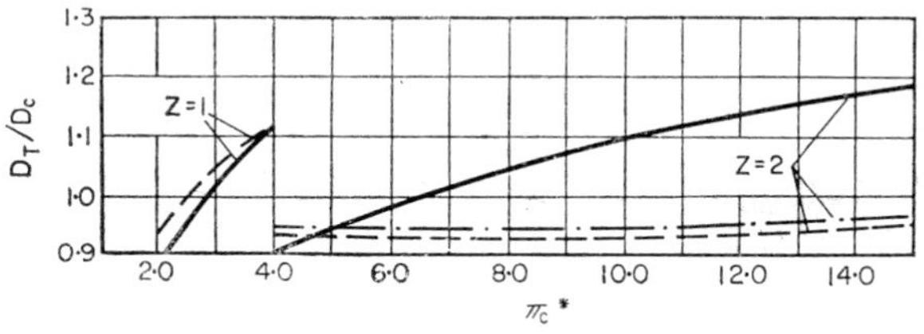

Fig. 44. Dependence of turbine diameter on π_c^* for $M_H = 2{\cdot}5$; $\eta_c^* = 0{\cdot}83$; $\eta_t^* = 0{\cdot}91$.

———— $\sigma_p = 2800$ kg/cm² = const.;

— — — — $\sigma_p = 2800 \dfrac{\sigma_p}{\sigma_{p0}}$ (for $T_H^*/T_g^* = 0{\cdot}4$);

— — — — $\sigma_p = 2800 \dfrac{\sigma_p}{\sigma_{p0}}$ (for $T_H^*/T_g^* = 0{\cdot}35$).

It can be seen from the curves shown in Fig. 44 that according to the extent of the increase in π_c^*, the value of D_t/D_c increases, which indicates the relative increase in the diameter of the turbine. An increase in the number of stages permits the diameter of the turbine to be substantially affected. If the possibility be taken into consideration of increasing the stress according to the extent of increase in π_c^*, then for large values of π_c^* this also exerts a large influence on the diameter of the turbine, which is shown in Fig. 44 for $T_H^*/T_g^* = 0{\cdot}35$ and $T_H^*/T_g^* = 0{\cdot}4$.

The value of $\sigma_p/\sigma_{p0} = f/\pi_c^*$ has been taken according to the data of Figs. 39 and 40.

Conclusions

1. For specified values of the efficiencies of the units of turbo-jet engines, and also of altitude and flight velocity, the efficiency of a turbo-jet engine is a function of the expansion ratio in the compressor and of the gas temperature prior to the turbine, the optimum value of which is determined by the system of equations

$$\frac{\partial C_R}{\partial \pi_c^*} = 0 \text{ and } \frac{\partial C_R}{\partial T_g^*} = 0\,.$$

In the present work it has been demonstrated that for an independent variation of π_c^* and T_g^* and for sufficiently high efficiencies, this system of equations has a congruent solution for $T_g^* \to \infty$ and $\pi_c^* \to \infty$.

It has also been shown that each of the equations $\partial C_R/\partial \pi_c^* = 0$ and $\partial C_R/\partial T_g^* = 0$ can be solved only in the implicit form if additional assumptions are not introduced.

2. The optimum expansion ratio with respect to efficiency, determined from the equation $\partial C_R/\partial \pi_c^* = 0$, considerably (by a factor of 1·7 – 2·0) exceeds the expansion ratio in magnitude, for which a given gas temperature is optimum. As a result of this the value of C_R, corresponding to the optimum value of π_c^*, is always found in that part of the curve of $C_R = f\,(T_g^*)$ where C_R increases for a reduction in T_g^*.

Moreover, even the temperature of the gas in modern engines will be optimum at sufficiently high expansion ratios, which rapidly increase with increase in T_g^*. Therefore, it can be assumed that the highest expansion ratio of practical advantage for use in turbo-jet engines is that for which a specified gas temperature becomes optimum.

3. The method used in this work for studying turbo-jet engines by the application of the complex parameter

$$\Pi = \frac{u_c^2\,\overline{G}_c}{\sigma_p q(\lambda_t)} = f\left(\pi_c^*\,;\ \frac{T_H^*}{T_g^*}\right)$$

connecting the basic aerodynamic and structural data for the compressor and turbine with the engine parameters π_c^* and T_g^*, and also with the altitude and flight speed T_H^* is of a general nature and enables rational data for the primary units and parameters to be developed in engines of a different type. In particular, with the aid of this method it has been shown that for high supersonic flight speeds, the output of the compressor in a turbo-jet engine is limited in the case when high peripheral speeds are used in it. This limitation is reduced only with increase of the gas temperature and of the stress in the turbine blades.

Comparison of the dimensions of engines for large values of M_H can be more expediently carried out on the assumption that the quantity $u_c^2/\sigma_p\, q\,(\lambda_t)$ remains constant, but the efficiency factor $\overline{G}_c$ is varied just as the whole complex parameter. With this method of comparison, the dimensions of the turbo-compressor section of an engine should be reduced with increase in the gas temperature, not only because of the increase in the specific thrust, but also in consequence of the increase in the efficiency factor of the compressor.

Literature

1. **Vukalovich M. P., Kirillin V. A.** *et al. Thermodynamic Properties of Gases (Termodinamicheskiye Svoistva Gazov)*, Mashgiz, 1953.
2. **Inozemtsev N. V.** *Aircraft Gas-turbine Engines (Aviatsionnyye Gazoturbinnyye Dvigateli)*, Oborongiz, 1955.
3. **Kulagin I. I.** *Theory of Aircraft Gas-turbine Engines (Teoriya Aviatsionnykh Gazoturbinnykh Dvigatelei)*, Oborongiz, 1955.
4. **Mel'kumov T. M.** *Theory of High-speed Engines with Auotignition (Teoriya Bystrokhodnogo Dvigatelya s Samovosplameneniyem)*, Oborongiz, 1953.
5. **Stechkin B. S., Kazandzhan P. K., Alekseyev A. P., Govorov A. N., Konovalov N. Ye., Nechayev N. N., Fedorov R. M.,** *Theory of Jet propulsion Engines,* Parts I and II *(Teoriya Reaktivnykh Dvigatelei,* ch. I i II pod redaktsiyei akademika Stechkina B. S.), edited by Academician Stechkin B. S., Oborongiz, 1954.

Index